The Green Diet

Mary Jolley

with Sarah J. Beesley, M.D.

Sourced Media Books

San Clemente, CA

Published by
Sourced Media Books
20 Via Cristobal
San Clemente, California 92673
www.sourcedmediabooks.com

ISBN: 978-0-9841068-2-0

Printed in the United States of America

Contents

Moist Banana Blueberry Pancakes, p. 89

To Mom,
The inspiration.

—Mary

The Green Diet

Four years ago, my mother went to the doctor for a routine check-up. She felt healthy. She wasn't overweight. She exercised for an hour a day, five times a week. And she ate a healthy diet filled with fruits and vegetables, whole grains, and only a limited amount of meat and dairy. She also avoided alcohol, tea, coffee, and tobacco. But to her surprise, her doctor broke some bad news: my mother's cholesterol was elevated, and she was probably going to have to go on medication—for the rest of her life. Because she was otherwise healthy (and already following the recommendations from the American Heart Association for reducing cardiovascular disease[1]), the doctor chalked up the rise in my mother's cholesterol to genetics.[2] She offered my mom the standard drug treatment but also mentioned an alternative: instead of medication, she could try eliminating animal products altogether. A holistic person by nature, my mother wanted to avoid medication if at all possible. So she decided to not only refrain from the intake of animal products, but also removed sugar, refined carbohydrates, and processed foods from her diet. She replaced these over-the-counter factory foods with the natural leafy greens, fresh fruits, and whole grains designed for our benefit by Mother Earth. And thus, The Green Diet was born.

One year later, my mother returned to the doctor. She had stuck to her new eating habits. She felt more fit, trim, energetic, and healthy. And best of all, the doctor happily reported that now, her cholesterol was ideal. The Green Diet worked. Mom has now been on The Green Diet for four years and believes that if there is a magic recipe for staying young and healthy, this is it. She has never felt better. Her immune system is stronger. She doesn't get sick as much. Her skin is radiant and youthful. She has an enviable amount of energy. She is wholly healthy. As a tribute to her, I have compiled the nutritional information of a plant-based diet, with recipes that celebrate her healthy way of life, in hopes that many others will discover the amazing benefits of The Green Diet.

What Is The Green Diet?

Plant-based diets are not a new idea or lifestyle. Notable people throughout history such as Plato, Leonardo da Vinci, Thomas Edison, Albert Einstein, Mahatma Gandhi, Benjamin Franklin, and countless others were advocates for vegetarianism.[3] Vegetarianism is the practice of excluding meat or game, fish, shellfish, and poultry from the diet. There are now several variations of the diet, with some also excluding eggs and other products produced from animal labor such as dairy and honey.

In 1944, when Donald Watson became frustrated that mainstream vegetarianism included dairy products, he founded the Vegan Society. He used the word "vegan" because he saw it as the beginning and the end of vegetarianism.[4] Veganism is more than a diet; it is also a lifestyle that endeavors to not use or consume animal products of any kind for food, clothing, or any other purpose. Typical vegans and vegetarians do, however, eat sugar and refined carbohydrates.

The Green Diet contains elements of vegetarianism and veganism, with an additional focus on eliminating refined sugars and carbohydrates. The Green Diet derives all of its prescribed foods from plant products, such as fruits, vegetables, legumes, whole grains, nuts, and oils. It also excludes sugar, artificial sweeteners, and refined carbohydrates. However, small amounts of natural sweeteners, such as honey and real maple syrup, are allowed.

The Green Diet also prohibits all animal products, including meat, dairy, eggs, and seafood. And The Green Diet further prescribes a healthy lifestyle by encouraging regular exercise and the avoidance of alcohol, tobacco, tea, and coffee.

Is The Green Diet Difficult to Follow?

As I began exploring The Green Diet, I assumed cutting out animal products and sugar would be impossible. But I knew that to fully understand and appreciate this way of eating, I would have to experience it myself. So I elected not only to research the value and possibilities of eating only plant-based foods, but to commit to living every aspect of The Green Diet for six weeks. My goal was to figure out how to be successful in getting all of the vitamins, minerals, and protein that I needed—and to feel satisfied and enjoy my meals at the same time.

The first morning of my "new life" was confusing; I didn't know what to eat for breakfast! Normally, I would have a bowl of cereal with milk, toast with butter, or eggs with bacon. Since all of those options were out, I resorted to a natural peanut butter and sugar-free jam sandwich on whole wheat bread. After that somewhat lackluster meal, I realized I had better stock up on food I would actually want to eat. I made a long trip to the grocery store and found plenty of interesting and exciting things to try. For lunch, I had a hummus and vegetable sandwich, and for dinner I made a vegetable stir fry. Delicious! Day one was a success—I was proud, happy, and full. Days two and three went by without much difficulty. I was having too much fun trying new things to miss the meat. However, when day five came, my husband was ready to head to his favorite hamburger place, and I felt like I could not even go for fear I might give in. I wanted a hamburger really badly! Fortunately, they had a veggie burger on the menu and it turned out to be delicious. Over time, I have found that most restaurants offer vegetarian entrees, and those that don't will usually accommodate a special request.

By week three, I had learned a few tricks and a couple of important lessons.

> Decreasing refined sugar intake and increasing intake of whole grains and fiber can decrease your risk of type II diabetes, another of the top causes of death in our country.
>
> —Sarah J. Beesley, M.D.

First, being prepared is the key to success. The Green Diet way of eating takes a bit more thought, especially at first. It can take more time and ingredients to prepare meals, so it is best to have the right foods handy. Nothing sabotages a diet like hunger, so stock up on green foods that are delicious and easy. My mom relies on salads and sprouts as quick staples.

Second, don't give in to peer pressure! One thing I discovered, and that my mother is well-familiar with, is that The Green Diet can be a bit socially isolating. At times, many people will not appreciate your healthy eating habits and may even try to pressure you to give up on your goal. By remaining confident that you are making the best choice for your body, and possibly even sharing some of the benefits you feel from your diet with others, you can resist the pressure you may feel. Fortunately, more and more people are learning about the multiple health and environmental benefits of eliminating meats and sugars and incorporating a plant-based diet.

As the weeks went by, it got easier to eat green and I felt much better. I noticed the biggest difference in the first two weeks as the toxins in my body were cleansed from my system. I felt more energetic. I slept better at night. I did not have sugar highs and lows. I lost five pounds. I felt more self-respect and balance. And I felt more in touch with nature. I understood what Einstein meant when he said, "Nothing will benefit human health and increase chances for survival of life on earth as much as the evolution to a vegetarian diet."[5]

After my experiment was over, I decided to eat a nice juicy filet of beef. I was surprised that the steak did not taste nearly as good as I remembered. Not long after finishing the filet, I had a terrible stomachache. I could literally feel the steak weighing me down and making me tired. I didn't feel healthy or happy. After six weeks without animal products, I was surprised at how drastically my body was affected. I realized The Green Diet worked.

Is This an "All-or-Nothing" Diet?

The Green Diet literally wiped out a genetic disease in my mom and has restored her perfect health. It makes me feel healthy and alive. It can lower your cholesterol, increase your heart health, improve your metabolism, and make you feel wholly healthy and reinvigorated. Scientists and nutritionists tout the many benefits of "going green," and each year, countless studies prove more and more harmful effects from refined carbohydrate and sugar consumption. Obviously, the closer you adhere to the diet, the more benefits you will see. Adhering to The Green Diet one hundred percent, as my mom does, will of course help you maximize its many benefits.

However, some people find the diet's regiments to be too extreme. It can be tricky to expect others to accommodate your dietary needs when you are a dinner guest or in a social setting. Many people value cultural traditions like turkey on Thanksgiving, lamb on Easter, and cake on birthdays that link us to our family, history, religion, and country. Dr. Sarah J. Beesley believes in the principle of "moderation in all things," and I consider an occasional deviation from the diet as "moderation" that is acceptable.

The Green Diet may not appeal to everyone, but I encourage you to give it a try, as I did, and enjoy its many rewards. Cleanse your body from harmful processed foods and toxins. Eat delicious, natural foods, straight from the earth. Receive all of the nutrients your body needs each day. Feel your bones and body become strong and invigorated. Embrace the way Mother Nature intended for us to eat.

With its nutritionally based step-by-step process, recipes, and meal plans, this book has all the tools you will need to explore The Green Diet successfully.

Bagel with Hummus and Veggies, p. 144

Step 1

Say "Goodbye" to Meat and Dairy, and "Hello" to Good Health

Cutting all meat and dairy out of the average American diet takes determination and self-control. But becoming aware of the incredible health benefits of a plant-based diet will draw the motivation needed to choose proteins like peas, beans, lentils, chickpeas, lettuces, sprouts, soymilk, tempeh, and texturized vegetable protein, instead of meat and dairy. These meat replacements are good sources of protein, as well as fiber, iron, calcium, zinc, and the B vitamins.[6] When followed, The Green Diet can provide all of the daily vitamins and nutrients needed, without exposure to the harmful cancer- and heart disease-causing components found in meat and dairy products. In this section, we will explore all of the lifestyle benefits of a green palate.

So Why Exactly Is "Going Green" So Good for Me?

When diagnosed with breast cancer five years ago, my friend Bonnie Hall began following a plant-based diet on her doctor's recommendation. Besides undergoing traditional medical treatment, she also changed her lifestyle. She is now 70 years old, vigorous, and healthy. When she started changing her diet, it was hard work and took discipline. She now feels it's easy. If she breaks from her diet, she gets a stomachache, as if her body is saying, "I don't like this."

Following The Green Diet will significantly help lower your risk of disease, cancer, and obesity. It also slows the aging process to keep you looking younger. Thanks to an abundance of scientific research that demonstrates the health and environmental benefits of a vegetarian diet, even the federal government recommends that we consume most of our calories from grain products, vegetables and fruits. And no wonder: an estimated 70 percent of all diseases, including one-third of all cancers, are related to diet.[7]

Amazingly, if you simply cut meat out of the standard American diet, you may be adding about thirteen healthy years to your life, says Michael F. Roizen, M.D., author of *The Real Age Diet: Make Yourself Younger with What You Eat*. "People who consume saturated, four-legged fat have a shorter life span and more disability at the end of their lives. Animal products clog your arteries, zap your energy and slow down your immune system. Meat eaters also experience accelerated cognitive and sexual dysfunction at a younger age.[8] Good nutrition generates more usable energy—energy to keep pace with the kids, tackle that home improvement project, or have better sex more often," Dr. Roizen says.

> In most cases of advanced disease, medical treatment should not be deferred while diet and lifestyle changes are undertaken, but the impact of these changes should also not be underestimated. For some diseases, especially coronary artery disease and type II diabetes, great benefit may come from a diet like The Green Diet combined with exercise.
>
> —*Sarah G. Beesley, M.D.*

Too much fat in your bloodstream means that arteries won't open properly and that your muscles won't get enough oxygen, resulting in fatigue. Balanced vegetarian diets are naturally free of artery-clogging, cholesterol-laden animal products that physically slow you down and keep you hitting the snooze button morning after morning. And because whole grains, legumes, fruits and vegetables are so high in complex carbohydrates, they supply the body with plenty of energizing fuel.[9]

The American Dietetic Association supports that an appropriately planned vegan diet is healthful, nutritionally adequate, and may prevent and help treat certain diseases in all stages of life.[10] A vegetarian diet reduces the risk for chronic degenerative diseases such as obesity, coronary artery disease, high blood pressure, diabetes, and colon, breast, prostate, stomach, lung and esophageal cancer.[11] Studies of vegetarians show that death rates from cancer are only about one-half to three-quarters of the general population's cancer-death rates.[12]

Vegetarians also tend to have lower blood pressure than non-vegetarians.[13] Some studies have shown that adding meat to a vegetarian diet raises blood pressure levels rapidly and significantly.[14]

A low-fat vegetarian diet is the single most effective way to stop the progression of coronary artery disease or prevent it entirely. Cardiovascular disease kills one million Americans annually and is the leading cause of death in the United States. But the mortality rate for cardiovascular disease is lower in vegetarians than in non-vegetarians. Bob Harper, a trainer on NBC's *The Biggest Loser,* recently switched to a vegetarian diet, resulting in a cholesterol drop of 100 points.[15]

Dr. Colin Campbell's China study supports mounting evidence showing that advanced heart disease, relatively advanced cancers, diabetes, and a few other degenerative diseases can potentially be reversed or halted by a plant-based diet. Campbell's laboratory has shown that cancer growth can be turned on and off by nutrition, despite genetic predisposition.[16] When asked what Dr. Campbell's prescription for good health is, he replied, "In short, it is about the multiple health benefits of consuming plant-based foods and the largely unappreciated health dangers of consuming animal-based foods, including all types of meat, dairy, and eggs."[17]

There are also many economic benefits to living The Green Diet. About 70 percent of all grain produced in the United States is fed to animals raised for slaughter. The seven billion livestock animals in the United States consume five times as much grain as is consumed directly by the American population. "If all the grain currently fed to livestock were consumed directly by people, the number of people who could be fed would be nearly 800 million," says David

Pimentel, professor of ecology at Cornell University. And if the grain were exported, it would boost the U.S. trade balance by $80 billion a year.[18] Meat accounts for 10 percent of Americans' food spending. Eating vegetables, grains, and fruits, in place of the 200 pounds of beef, chicken and fish every meat eater consumes annually, would cut individual food bills by an average of $4,000 per year.[19]

What Safety Benefits Come from a Plant-Based Diet?

Besides intrinsically being better for you, a vegetarian diet may also be safer to eat. According to the U.S. Food and Drug Administration (FDA), foods rich in protein such as meat, poultry, fish and seafood, are frequently involved in food-borne illness outbreaks.[20]

The Center for Disease Control and Prevention (CDC) reported a total of 1,270 food-related illnesses in 2006, resulting in 27,634 cases and 11 deaths. Norovirus was the most common disease, followed by Salmonella (18% of outbreaks and 3,252 cases). Among outbreaks caused by a single food vehicle, the most common food commodities to which outbreak-related cases were attributed were poultry (21%).[21] Eggs are loaded with saturated fat and cholesterol, and their fragile, porous shells are the perfect host for salmonella, the leading cause of food poisoning in America.[22] Further, the most toxic form of the poison arsenic is used in chicken feed to promote faster growth. The National Institute of Health warns that this cancer-causing chemical is likewise ingested by people who eat chicken meat.[23]

The Environmental Protection Agency (EPA) estimates that nearly 95 percent of the pesticide residue in the typical American diet comes from meat, fish, and dairy products.[24] Fish, in particular, contain carcinogens (PCBs, DDT) and heavy metals (mercury, arsenic, lead, cadmium) that can't be removed

> While lipid levels (including cholesterol) are not the only measure of a healthy lifestyle, they are a significant indicator for cardiac disease, the number one cause of death in the United States for both men and women.
>
> —*Sarah J. Beesley, M.D.*

through cooking or freezing. Meat and dairy products can also be laced with steroids and hormones.

The EPA revealed that women who ate fish just twice a week had blood mercury levels that were seven times higher than those of women who did not eat any fish.[25] Women who eat just one can of tuna per week are often 30 percent over the EPA cutoff for a safe mercury level. Mercury is known to possibly cause brain damage, memory loss, and damage to a developing fetus.[26] Plant foods like walnuts, flax seeds, chia seeds or vegetarian DHA supplements contain all the essential fatty acids that you need, without the harmful toxins found in fish.

But Don't I Need Milk?

A common misconception is that milk makes bones strong. However, a high intake of animal protein encourages the loss of calcium from the bones.[27] When there isn't enough calcium in the bloodstream, your body will leach it from existing bone. The metabolic result is that your skeleton will become porous and lose strength over time. People who live in countries where the typical diet is plant-based have little osteoporosis, even when calcium intake is lower than in dairy-consuming countries.[28] The calcium that animal proteins pull from the bones is excreted though the kidneys, not only increasing the risk of osteoporosis, but also increasing the risk of kidney stones. Researchers in England found that when people added 34 grams of protein (5 ounces of fish) to their normal diets, their risk of forming kidney stones rose by as much as 250 percent.[29] Dr. Campbell reassures that "as long as you are eating a variety of plant foods in sufficient quantity to maintain your weight, your body gets plenty of protein."[30]

Dairy may also be contributing to your allergies, skin problems, asthma, upset stomach, gas, diarrhea, or constipation. Milk is high in fat and low in iron, and is frequently contaminated with antibiotics, steroids, and growth hormones. By eliminating dairy, you are likely to experience major benefits, such as a drop in cholesterol, weight loss, and relief from allergies, asthma, indigestion, or chronic stomach problems.[31]

Isn't Protein Good for Me?

Protein is a vital component of our bodies, and there are hundreds of thousands of different kinds. They function as enzymes, hormones, structural tissue and transport molecules, all of which make life possible. One concern many people have about vegetarianism is that they may not be able to get the proper amount of protein without eating meat. But this is not true.

Proteins are constructed as long chains of amino acids. They wear out on a regular basis and must be replaced. When proteins are digested, they provide a new supply of amino acid building blocks. Through enormously complex metabolic systems, the human body can derive all the essential amino acids from the natural variety of plant proteins encountered every day. Plant protein allows for a slow and steady synthesis of new proteins. It doesn't require eating higher quantities of plant protein or meticulously planning every meal to acquire the desired amount of daily protein.[32] Actually, eating too much protein causes the body to take in more nitrogen than it needs. This places strain on the kidneys, which must expel the excess nitrogen through urine. That is the reason people with kidney disease are encouraged to eat low-protein diets to reduce nitrogen levels.[33]

According to the recommended daily allowance (RDA), you should get about 10 percent of your energy, or calories, from protein. And this is considerably more than the actual amount required. But because requirements may vary from individual to individual, 10 percent dietary protein is recommended to ensure adequate intake for the common majority.[34] Remarkably, the average American consumes 15–16 percent protein, placing them at higher risk for getting cancer.[35] Dr. Campbell found that protein, specifically casein (found in animal protein), promotes cancer growth. The 1997 report of the World Cancer Research Fund and American Institute for Cancer Research also noted that meaty, high-protein diets were linked to some types of cancer.[36] However, in these experiments, plant protein did not promote cancer growth. Replacing animal protein with plant protein also lowers blood cholesterol levels, even if the amount and type of fat stays the same.[37]

Although soy can be a good protein alternative to meat, be cautious about consuming too much of it. Little is known about its effect on breast cancer and memory loss. Avoid pills that deliver concentrated soy protein or pure isoflavones.[38] Two to four servings a week of soy-based food such as tofu or soy milk is a good target and should be enough.

Let's Cut to the Chase: Is This Diet Going to Help Me Lose Weight?

The standard American diet—high in saturated fats and processed foods, and low in plant-based foods and complex carbohydrates—is making Americans fat while slowly killing them. According to the CDC and the National Center for Health Statistics, 64 percent of adults and 15 percent of children ages 6 to 19 are overweight and are at risk of weight-related ailments, including heart disease, stroke and diabetes.[39]

Population studies show that meat eaters have three times the obesity rate of vegetarians and nine times the obesity rate of vegans. Adult vegans are, on average, 10 to 20 pounds lighter than adult meat eaters.[40] Animal products are usually high in fat; even "lean" cuts of meat have more fat than a healthy body needs.[41] Chickens are now bred and given drugs to grow abnormally large, and as a result, chicken flesh today contains three times as much fat as it did just 35 years ago.[42]

Animal products also lack fiber. Fiber helps make food more satisfying without adding many calories, and it is only found in plant foods.[43] The only weight-loss plan that has been scientifically proven to take weight off, and keep it off for more than a year, is a vegan diet.[44]

A study conducted from 1986 to 1992 by Dean Ornish, M.D., president and director of the Preventive Medicine Research Institute, found that overweight people who followed a low-fat, vegetarian diet lost an average of 24 pounds in the first year and kept off that weight

---

High dietary fat and high alcohol diets may increase the risk of breast cancer in post-menopausal women.

—*Sarah J. Beesley, M.D.*

five years later. Even better, they lost the weight without counting calories or carbohydrates, measuring portions, or feeling hungry.[45]

Many plant foods also contain nutrients beneficial to premenopausal and menopausal women. Certain foods are rich in phytoestrogens, the plant-based chemical compounds that mimic the behavior of estrogen. Since phytoestrogens can increase estrogen and progesterone levels, maintaining a balance of them in your diet helps ensure a more comfortable passage through menopause. Soy is by far the most abundant natural source of phytoestrogens, but these compounds also can be found in hundreds of other foods, such as apples, beets, cherries, dates, garlic, olives, plums, raspberries, squash and yams. Because menopause is also associated with weight gain and a slowed metabolism, a low-fat, high-fiber vegetarian diet can help ward off extra pounds for women.

There are many weight loss programs out there that can be very harmful to your health. High-protein diets are not only unnatural in their aversion to the many benefits of plant-based foods, but they can be dangerous. After Dr. Atkins died, a vegetarian group obtained his medical records and gave them to *The Wall Street Journal,* which reported that he weighed 258 pounds and had signs of congestive heart failure.[46] Beware of diets that may help you to lose weight in the short run but can be devastating to your overall happiness and quality of life.

Anything Else? How About Eternal Youth?

Residents of Okinawa, Japan, have the longest life expectancy of any Japanese region and likely the longest life expectancy of anyone in the world, according to a 30-year study of more than 600 Okinawan centenarians.[47] Their secret: a low-calorie diet of unrefined complex carbohydrates, fiber-rich fruits and vegetables, and soy—much like The Green Diet.

An animal-free diet is scientifically better for your heart, your health, and your lifespan. So in the interest of a better life, give up the meat and dairy. Go green!

Grilled Artichokes, p. 158

Step 2

Mother Nature's Gifts: Fruits and Vegetables

It's no accident that fruits and vegetables are arguably the most beautiful natural food found on earth. Mother Nature intended to attract humans to their beneficial bounty before languages and food pyramids were ever formed. No other food group can provide more natural vitamins and minerals to the body than these beautiful plants.

When it comes to recommended serving sizes for fruits and vegetables, indulgence is allowed. More is always better. People in the top tier of fruit and vegetable consumption (about 35 servings a week, or your basic five a day) are 15 percent less likely to have a heart attack or other problem caused by restricted blood flow to the heart muscle than those in the bottom tier.[48] Fruits and vegetables also help protect against eye disease and bowel trouble. They have also been proven to work against specific cancers, such as bladder, colon and rectal, and prostate. And people who habitually eat lower on the food chain tend to have fewer instances of constipation, hemorrhoids, and diverticulitis.[49]

Come Partake of Nature's Bountiful Rainbow . . .

Disease-fighting phytochemicals give fruits and vegetables their rich, varied hues. They come in two main classes: carotenoids and anthocyanins. Rich yellow and orange fruits and vegetables—carrots, oranges, sweet potatoes, mangoes, pumpkins, corn—owe their color to carotenoids. Leafy green vegetables are also rich in carotenoids, but they get their green color from chlorophyll. Red, blue and purple fruits and vegetables—plums, cherries, red bell peppers—contain anthocyanins.[50] Therefore, cooking with a rainbow of colors is a good way to ensure you're eating a variety of naturally occurring substances that boost immunity and prevent a range of illnesses.

Strive to consume three daily servings of fruit and four servings of vegetables at minimum. But it never hurts to shoot for more. Select your produce for variety and color. On most days, try to intake at least one serving from each of the following fruit and vegetable groups: dark green leafy vegetables, yellow or orange fruits and vegetables, red fruits and vegetables, legumes and peas, and citrus fruits.

> Just to give you an idea, a serving of vegetables could be five cherry tomatoes, five sticks of celery or a whole carrot. A serving of fruit would be a medium apple, half a banana or fifteen grapes.
>
> —*Sarah J. Beesley, M.D.*

When selecting fruits and vegetables, choose fresh rather than canned whenever possible. Additionally, try to eat your produce raw as much as possible to increase vitamin intake, as some vitamins, such as vitamin C and folic acid, are sensitive to heat. Frozen fruits and vegetables are nearly as good as fresh—and may even be better in some cases when the comparative "fresh" produce has been stored for weeks or months under conditions that prevent natural ripening.[51]

. . . And Reap the Many Rewards

There is no doubt that fruits and vegetables are loaded with vitamins and minerals that are good for the heart, mind, and body. However, identifying the specific benefits of individual fruits and vegetables can be tricky, as the chemical composition of plants varies based on factors such as the season, the soil, its watering history, the pests and pesticides to which it was exposed, its degree of ripening when picked and eaten, and under what conditions it was stored, processed and cooked. But scientists have conclusively isolated a number of substances that plants make or store that play critical roles in keeping us healthy.

Vitamins

By definition, vitamins are carbon-containing compounds that the body needs in small amounts to maintain its tissue and keep the metabolism humming. More and more it looks as though cancer, heart disease, stroke, diabetes, osteoporosis, and other chronic diseases are, in part, diseases of vitamin deficiency.[52] Inadequate folic acid is emerging as a risk factor for heart disease and some cancers. Low consumption of a special class of vitamins—antioxidants, which capture and neutralize free radicals—appear to be involved in the early stages of heart disease, cancer, aging-related eye disease, dementia, and possibly aging itself.[53] Extensive research has been done on vitamins and minerals; it is important to understand their incredible role in keeping our bodies healthy.

Vitamins are either fat soluble (vitamins A, D, E, and K) or water soluble (vitamins C, Bs, folate, and pantothenic acid). A fat-soluble vitamin is a vitamin that can dissolve in dietary fats. A certain amount of fat is needed in the diet to help the body absorb these vitamins.

Any excess fat-soluble vitamins are stored in the liver. Enough of the vitamins A and D are stored in the liver of a well-nourished person to satisfy the body's needs for several months if they are absent from the diet. But if the diet contains too much vitamin A or D, the surplus may be harmful. Such excessive intake is less likely to result from overeating

Vegetables, including cooked tomatoes which contain lycopene, may help protect against prostate cancer. Adversely, high-fat diets, especially those loaded with animal fat and red meat consumption, have been associated with an increased risk in prostate cancer in multiple studies.

—Sarah J. Beesley, M.D.

than through overzealous use of vitamin pills. That's why it is best to rely mostly on fresh fruit and vegetable consumption for one's daily vitamin dosage.

Water-soluble vitamins are not stored in the body and must be replaced each day by a continuous supply through food. Water-soluble vitamins dissolve in water and are eliminated in urine. They

> Fat-soluble and water-soluble vitamins are absorbed in different parts of the GI tract. If you have had surgery to the small bowel or stomach, or have certain kinds of GI diseases, you may be at an increased risk for vitamin deficiency.
>
> —*Sarah J. Beesley, M.D.*

are easily destroyed or washed out during food storage, preparation, and cooking. Proper storage and preparation of food can minimize vitamin loss. For example, steaming vegetables retains more vitamins than boiling. The water used to cook vegetables in is packed with vitamins and makes a great, vitamin-rich broth for soups. Refrigerating fresh produce and keeping grains away from strong light can also help hold in the vitamins.

On the next few pages, let's explore the many nutritional benefits of the vitamins found in plant-based foods.

Fat-Soluble Vitamins

Vitamin A

Beta carotene is converted to vitamin A by the human body.[54] You can look for vitamin A in natural orange foods such as carrots, sweet potatoes, pumpkins, and apricots. Leafy green vegetables are also good sources of vitamin A.[55]

Vitamin A helps with night vision, protein formation, immune function, embryonic development, reproduction, bone metabolism, skin health, reducing the risk of heart disease and cancer, and antioxidant activity.[56]

It is relatively easy to get too much vitamin A from supplements. When shopping for a multivitamin, look for one that gets all or most of its vitamin A activity from beta carotene, not preformed vitamin A. Too much preformed vitamin A can block the effects of vitamin D and lead to liver damage.[57]

Vitamin D

Plants aren't the only things that need sunlight to thrive—our bodies convert the sun's rays into vitamin D. Vitamin D plays an important role in the maintenance of organ systems. Vitamin D regulates the calcium and phosphorus levels in the blood by promoting their absorption from food in the intestines, and by promoting reabsorption of calcium in the kidneys. Without vitamin D, only about 10 to 15 percent of dietary calcium and about 60 percent of phosphorus is absorbed.[58]

Vitamin D also promotes bone formation and mineralization and is essential in the development of an intact and strong skeleton. Before birth and during childhood, vitamin D deficiency can cause slowed growth and skeletal deformities and increase the risk of hip fracture later in life. Deficiency in adults causes muscle weakness and an increased risk of osteoporosis.[59] Today vitamin D deficiency is common among both children and adults.

Additionally, the immune system benefits by vitamin D as it promotes anti-tumor activity. It strongly inhibits the growth and reproduction of a variety of cancer cells,[60] including those from breast, ovary, colon, prostate, and brain.[61] Cancer patients who undergo treatments in the summer, and therefore intake more vitamin D from the sun, may have a better chance of surviving their disease

---

According to several studies, 30–50 percent of men and women of all ages may be vitamin D deficient, despite taking a multivitamin and eating fortified foods. Sensible sun exposure and vitamin D supplementation are most likely needed to fulfill the body's vitamin D requirement.

—Sarah J. Beesley, M.D.

than those who undergo treatment in the winter when they are less exposed to sunlight.[62]

Vitamin D signals muscle cells to make new protein. This can strengthen muscles and improve stability, especially in older people. Getting vitamin D, especially from sunlight, helps lower blood pressure. Multiple sclerosis, Hodgkin's lymphoma, and many types of cancer are more common in areas where people have low access to vitamin D.

Adequate sun exposure alone can provide enough vitamin D.[63] However, seasonal changes, geographic latitude, cloud cover, smog, daily schedules, skin color, and the use of sunscreen can limit UV ray exposure and vitamin D synthesis in the skin.[64] It is important for individuals with limited sun exposure to include good sources of vitamin D in their diet and take a supplement. Few foods are naturally rich in vitamin D, so you will get most of your vitamin D intake in the form of fortified products, including soy milk and cereal grains or supplements. One of the best natural sources of vitamin D is sun-dried shiitake mushrooms.

Vitamin E

High doses of vitamin E help block the harmful effects of LDL cholesterol and may reduce the risk of coronary disease.[65] Additionally, vitamin E is traditionally considered the most active biological antioxidant in humans.[66]

Taking antibiotics for a bacterial infection can also kill the bacteria that normally live in the intestines, decreasing the amount of vitamin K available to your liver for the creation of clotting factors. This is not normally a problem as the bacteria will recolonize after the antibiotics are stopped, but if you are taking other medications that also decrease vitamin K availability, like Coumadin, or Warfarin, you may have a temporary increase in your risk for bleeding.

—*Sarah J. Beesley, M.D.*

Vitamin E is abundant in vegetable oils and leafy vegetables. Whole grains and nuts are also good sources.[67] There is no evidence of adverse effects of vitamin E naturally occurring in foods. The upper limit warning for vitamin E applies to any form obtained from supplements or fortified foods.

Vitamin K

Naturally produced by the bacteria in the intestines, vitamin K plays an essential role in normal blood clotting, promotes bone health, and helps form some proteins in the body.[68] Dark green leafy vegetables, cauliflower, and soybeans are good sources of vitamin K.[69] Although a tolerable upper intake level has not been established for vitamin K, excessive amounts can cause the breakdown of red blood cells and liver damage. Large doses are not advised.

Water-Soluble Vitamins

Vitamin C

Vitamin C serves many purposes as it holds body cells together, aids in wound healing, assists in bone and tooth formation, strengthens the blood vessel walls, is vital for the function of the immune system, and improves absorption and utilization of iron.[70] Vitamin C serves as an antioxidant. It also helps prevent nutritional ailments such as scurvy, the disease that did the most to bring public attention to vitamin deficiency diseases, as well as cause plenty of pirates to experience dental problems.

Our bodies do not naturally make vitamin C. Although the body has a constant need for vitamin C, it has a limited storage ca-

---

Vitamin C is found in a wide variety of fruits and vegetables. Diseases like scurvy are now uncommon, as most people have access to fresh produce year-round.

—*Sarah G. Beesley, M.D.*

pacity, so a regular and adequate intake is essential. Citrus, broccoli, strawberries, and dark green vegetables are common sources of vitamin C.[71]

Some conditions have been shown to elevate the vitamin C requirement: environmental stress, use of certain drugs (such as oral contraceptives), tissue healing of wounds, growth (children and pregnant women), fever and infection, and smoking.[72] In sickness and in health, vitamin C is most definitely an essential daily vitamin.

B Vitamins

Eight of the water-soluble vitamins comprise the B-complex group: thiamin (vitamin B1), riboflavin (vitamin B2), niacin, vitamin B6, folate, vitamin B12, biotin and pantothenic acid. Most B vitamins are widely distributed in foods, and their influence is felt in many parts of the body.

Thiamin is important in key reactions involved in the metabolism of carbohydrates to supply energy. It helps promote normal appetite and helps the nervous system function. Look for thiamin in whole grains, dried beans, and nuts.[73]

Riboflavin helps release energy from foods; it is a coenzyme in numerous redox reactions and required for a wide variety of cellular processes. Food sources are leafy greens, beans, and nuts.[74]

Niacin is important in many metabolic processes in the body including carbohydrate and fatty acid metabolism and tissue respiration. High levels have been shown to reduce harmful LDL blood cholesterol levels while increasing healthy HDL cholesterol levels.[75] Nuts and beans are good sources of niacin.

Vitamin B6 is important in protein metabolism and the utilization of fats and carbohydrates. It helps the immune system and may help limit pain in certain medical conditions, such as PMS and carpal tunnel syndrome. The classic signs of too little B6 are inflammation of the skin, anemia, depression and confusion, and convulsions. Meat and legumes are the major food sources of vitamin B6; so when following The Green Diet, as you decrease your consumption of red meat, it is important to increase your legume intake. No adverse effects associated with the consumption of vitamin B6 from food have been reported.

Vitamin B12 is needed for the formation of red blood cells and for healthy nervous and immune systems. Because 10 to 30 percent of people over the age of 50 may not absorb food-bound vitamin B12 well, it is advisable for those older than 50 to meet their RDA (recommended daily allowance) mainly by consuming foods fortified with B12 or a supplement containing vitamin B12.

The B12 vitamin is of note because it is not available from plant products, making B12 deficiency a concern for vegetarians. Good sources of B12 include vitamins, fortified cereals, and fortified soymilk.

Folate, or folic acid, helps in the regulation of cell division and may be involved in reversing some cell damage. It is needed for the formation of red blood cells. Folate has also been identified as a nutrient that helps prevent anemia.

Folic acid is very important for all women who may become pregnant. Adequate folate intake during the time just before and just after a woman becomes pregnant helps protect against a number of birth defects, including neural tube defects like spina bifida.[76] In a randomized trial, a high-dose folic acid supplement reduced the incidence of recurrent neural-tube defects by 70 percent.[77] The RDA for folate equivalents for pregnant women is 600–800 micrograms, which is twice the normal RDA of 400 micrograms for women who are not pregnant. Recent research has shown that folate is also very important for men who are planning on fathering children; it can reduce the risk of birth defects.

Substantial evidence suggests that low folic acid intake increases the risk of cardiovascular disease and several types of cancer.[78] Homocysteine is an amino acid in the blood that is related to a higher risk of coronary heart disease and stroke.[79] Folic acid, and to

> Folate supplementation is extremely important for anyone who might have the possibility of becoming pregnant. Ideally, the supplements should be started before conception as the greatest benefit to the fetus is in the earliest portion of the pregnancy, often before the woman is even aware she is pregnant.
>
> —Sarah G. Beesley, M.D.

a lesser extent vitamin B6 and vitamin B12,[80] help break down homocysteine in the blood.[81] Higher intake of folic acid is associated with a lower risk of colon cancer and breast cancer, particularly among people who drink alcohol daily (alcohol interferes with folate absorption and metabolism).[82] Folate can be found in leafy green vegetables, whole grains, and a variety of fruits and beans.

> An uncommon cause of cognitive and other neurologic deficits is vitamin B12 deficiency. Along with folate deficiency, B12 deficiency can also cause anemia.
>
> —*Sarah J. Beesley, M.D.*

Pantothenic Acid

Pantothenic acid is critical in the metabolism and synthesis of carbohydrates, proteins, and fats. Its name is derived from the Greek pantothen meaning "from everywhere." Small quantities of pantothenic acid are found in nearly every food, with high amounts in whole-grain cereals and legumes.[83]

Minerals

The minerals that are important for the nutrition of our bodies can be divided into three categories. First, there are minerals which are stored in the body in large amounts: sodium (Na), potassium (K), calcium (Ca), magnesium (Mg), and phosphorus (P). Second, there are trace minerals that have a known importance to our nutrition: iron (Fe), zinc (Zn), copper (Cu), iodine (I), fluoride (F), selenium (Se), and chromium (Cr). And third, there are trace minerals important to our nutrition but their exact role in nutrition is not known: cobalt (Co), molybdenum (Mo), manganese (Mn), cadmium (Cd), arsenic (As), silicon (Si), vanadium (V), and nickel (Ni).

Calcium

Calcium helps us build strong bones and teeth. Calcium helps to lower blood pressure and cholesterol.[84] It also helps with muscle contraction, nerve transmission, blood clotting, and normal heart functioning.[85] Calcium can help prevent osteoporosis, especially in postmenopausal women and older men. While a lifelong deficit can affect bone and tooth formation, over-retention can cause hypercalcemia (elevated levels of calcium in the blood), impaired kidney function, and decreased absorption of other minerals. Diets that are high in protein cause calcium to be lost through urine, leading to higher instances of kidney stones. Protein from animal products is more likely to cause calcium loss than protein from plant foods, one reason that vegetarians tend to have stronger bones than meat eaters.

Vitamin D is needed to absorb calcium. Calcium supplements are used to prevent and treat calcium deficiencies. Most experts recommend that supplements be taken with food and that no more than 600 mg should be taken at a time because the percent of calcium absorbed decreases as the amount of calcium in the supplement increases. It is recommended to spread doses throughout the day. Common food sources of calcium are broccoli, spinach and other dark green leafy vegetables.

> Osteoporosis is often thought of as a disease that only affects women, but one third of hip fractures (a major indicator of osteoporosis) occur in men—and the mortality rate in the year after a fracture is greater for men. Often enough calcium and vitamin D cannot be obtained from the diet alone, even with a traditional American diet. Supplementation is likely beneficial to all men and women.
>
> —*Sarah J. Beesley, M.D.*

Copper

Copper is essential in all plants and animals. Copper is carried mostly in the bloodstream, and when it is first absorbed in the stomach it is transported to the liver. It has roles as an enzyme and also as an electron transporter. It is believed that zinc and copper compete for absorption in the digestive tract, so a diet that is excessive in one of these minerals may result in a deficiency in the other. Because of its role in facilitating iron uptake, copper deficiency can often produce anemia-like symptoms. Cashews, sunflower seeds, and whole grain products are good sources of copper.

Iron

Iron combines with protein to form hemoglobin (a part of red blood cells), which aids in the transport of oxygen to the body. Iron strengthens chemical links to the brain and helps prevent anemia. Iron-poor blood can leave a person pale, fatigued, and mentally dull. Lack of iron stunts growth and development of children and can damage long-term thinking skills. Some good green sources of dietary iron include lentils, beans, leaf vegetables, tofu, chickpeas, black-eyed peas, potatoes with skin, bread made from completely whole-grain flour, and molasses.

Your body closely regulates iron uptake. However, your body cannot regulate the absorption of iron from meat as carefully as it does from plants and supplements. If your iron storehouse is well stocked, the kind of iron in plants and supplements will pass through your body. The iron in meat, though, seems to slide under this mineral radar and add to the stockpile. Your body has no regulated physiological means of excreting iron. Excessive levels of iron in the blood can damage DNA, as well as the cells of the gastrointestinal tract, heart, liver, and elsewhere.

Magnesium

Magnesium is similar in function to calcium and phosphorus.[86] Magnesium is essential to all cells of all known living organisms. It plays a vital role in glucose metabolism and is important in maintaining normal muscle functions, nerve conduction, and synthesis of fats and proteins. Unfortunately, studies indicate that many Americans are magnesium deficient. Lack of magnesium forces the body to work harder to accomplish even low-intensity activities. Magnesium is a vital component of a healthy human diet, and magnesium deficiency has been implicated in a number of human diseases.

Magnesium is readily available in many common foods such as nuts, beans, unpolished grains, and leafy green vegetables. Excess magnesium in the blood is freely filtered at the kidneys, and for this reason it is very difficult to overdose on magnesium from dietary sources alone.

Phosphorus

Phosphorus helps build strong bones and teeth. It is important in muscle contraction and helps the body utilize carbohydrates and fats. Phosphorus is important in maintaining pH and in the storage and transfer of energy. Whole grain products are a great source of phosphorus. Overconsumption can cause skeletal porosity, interference with calcium absorption, and bone demineralization.

Potassium

Potassium is the most abundant positively charged particle inside your cells. Potassium is important to brain and nerve function, cell metabolism, enzyme reactions and synthesis of muscle protein. It is necessary for normal muscle activity. Potassium maintains fluid volume inside and outside of cells and thus normal cell function. It acts to blunt the rise of blood pressure in response to excess sodium intake and decrease markers of bone turnover and recurrence of kidney stones.[87]

Your body regulates the concentration of potassium very carefully, because too much or too little can cause problems. A drop in potassium can make you feel weak and tired, trigger extra heartbeats (especially in people who already have heart disease), and cause muscle cramps or pain. Diets based on processed foods are high in sodium and low in potassium, whereas diets abundant in natural foods, such as fruits and vegetables, are low in sodium and rich in potassium.[88] Beans, beets, potatoes, melon, apricots, bananas, and raisins are great sources of potassium.

Sodium

The human requirement for sodium in the diet is about 500 mg per day, which is typically less than a tenth as much as many diet's daily "seasoned to taste." Most people consume far more sodium than is physiologically needed. Processed food (such as canned soups and vegetables, cheese, pickles, hot dogs, cereals, chips) and beverages commonly contain high amount of sodium. Sodium is necessary for normal body function relating to regulation of fluid volume and proper cell membrane function. However, excessive intake of sodium can result in hypertension (high blood pressure).[89]

Zinc

Zinc is involved in most metabolic processes. It influences growth, sexual maturity, and normal wound healing.[90] It may help prevent the growth of abnormal cells associated with cancer and other diseases. Zinc ions are now considered to be neurotransmitters. Clinical studies have found that zinc, combined with antioxidants, may delay the progression of age-related macular degeneration. Significant dietary intake of zinc has recently been shown to impede the onset of flu. Zinc deficiency during pregnancy can negatively affect both the mother and the baby. Cognitive and motor function may also be impaired in zinc-deprived children. Even though zinc is an essential requirement for a healthy body, too much zinc can be harmful. Excessive absorption of zinc can also suppress copper and iron absorption.

Zinc absorption is lower for those consuming vegetarian diets than for those eating non-vegetarian diets. Therefore, it is suggested that the zinc requirement for those consuming a vegetarian diet is approximately twice as much than for those consuming a nonvegetarian diet. Look for zinc in almonds, peanuts, chickpeas, and soy products.

As we see, plant-based foods are loaded with all of the vitamins and minerals our bodies need to develop properly. They will help fight disease and clean the toxins from our systems to restore our health. By partaking of these foods that Mother Nature intended for us, we can enjoy beautiful, invigorating meals.

Garden Pasta Salad, p. 116

Step 3

Banish Sugar and Embrace Whole Grains

We are probably all too familiar with the many sources of sugar. Sugar comes in many forms including white sugar, brown sugar, cane sugar, sugar in the raw, high fructose corn syrup, candies, soda, jams, ketchup, baked goods, juice, several packaged foods and low-fat products for added taste. Refined flour, chips, pretzels, muffins, white rice and pasta also end up as sugar in your body.

So What's So Bad About Sugar?

While it may taste good at first, sugar offers no benefits beyond its taste. Sugar weakens the immune system. White blood cell counts are suppressed after sugar consumption. White blood cells are the body's first line of defense against an invading virus or bacteria, so this leaves you susceptible to illness, especially with regular consumption of sugar.

Aging is accelerated by sugar consumption through a process called glycation. When this occurs, tissue elasticity reduces to cause skin sagging, arterial stiffness and poor organ function. Sugar also causes the brain, nervous system and eyes to age. It can lead to tooth decay and gum disease.[91] In addition, sugar feeds cancer cells, supplying the energy needed for them to multiply quickly. Sure, it may taste good, tempt, and give you a "high," but is it really worth it?

Most foods containing refined sugar have little to no nutrients and are "empty calories," which is one reason why after your "sugar high" disappears, you never feel satisfied after eating them. When you eat foods high in sugar (glucose), the glucose enters the bloodstream, causing blood sugars to quickly rise. The pancreas responds by secreting insulin which then causes a surge of sugars to enter the cells to either be used as energy or stored as fat for later use. Insulin is secreted in proportion to the amount of sugar consumed, and insulin instructs the body to store extra energy (glucose) as fat. Blood sugars then fall to normal or possibly just below normal levels. While this is happening, you experience a "sugar rush" of hyperactivity only to be followed by the "crash," characterized by fatigue, drowsiness and poor concentration. Naturally, as blood sugars fall, the body works to maintain balance by causing a craving for more sugar—and the whole process starts all over again.

Repeatedly eating sugar throughout the day leads to chronically high insulin and ultimately, an insulin resistance. At this point, weight loss becomes extremely difficult and there is often an increase in blood pressure, cholesterol, abdominal fat, and cancer risk. If the pancreas does not produce enough insulin, the glucose stays in the bloodstream and, over time, leads to type II diabetes.

All foods containing carbohydrates in any form are digested and eventually become simple sugars that the body will reorganize and store as a different form of carbohydrate or as fat. Depending on whether the starting starch is an already refined sugar or a complex whole grain, the body will react to release more or less insulin which determines how your calories are processed and stored. If you eat a meal high in refined sugars, causing high insulin levels, the extra calories can be stored as fat. This happens because the body's starch storage capacity can become saturated, forcing the body to convert sugar to triglycerides (i.e., fat) which your body has an endless capacity to store.

—*Sarah G. Beesley, M.D.*

Okay, So What's So Great About Whole Grains?

Eating whole grains helps protect against the development of type II diabetes.[92] Whole grains also help protect against cancer and heart disease,[93] and they improve gastrointestinal health, too.[94] Whole grains have a low, slow, steady effect on blood sugar and insulin levels, which essentially cause you to feel full longer than refined carbohydrates do. This natural effect also helps you stay in control of your weight, energy levels, and mood.

Whole grains are an essential part of The Green Diet. They provide a tasty, filling staple to your meals. Whole grains include whole wheat bread, brown rice, whole wheat tortillas, whole grain pastas, corn, millet, barley, and wheat berries. You should strive for five servings of whole grains a day. Replacing refined grains with whole grains can help you lose weight.[95]

When grocery shopping, ensure that you are getting whole grains instead of refined grains. Check the labels to see that the first ingredient listed on a product is a whole grain, and build each of your meals around a hearty grain dish. Grains are rich in vitamins and minerals, as well as fiber and protein.

> Half of a whole grain bagel, one slice of whole wheat bread, or one half cup of whole grain pasta are each equal to one serving of whole grains.
>
> —*Sarah G. Beesley, M.D.*

So What About Sugar Substitutes?

Despite what many diets may say, artificial and chemical sweeteners are unnatural and might even be worse for your body than sugar.[96] Saccharin was the first artificial sweetener developed. Though it can still be found in some gums and toothpastes, it is no longer permitted to be added to foods because it was found to be related to bladder cancer.[97]

Aspartame is still approved by the FDA, under controversial circumstances, and is common in "diet" or "sugar-free" food and beverages. But the FDA has received complaints that aspartame causes headaches, vomiting, mood changes, blurred vision, fatigue, sleep problems and much more.[98] When aspartame is broken down in the body, methanol is produced. Methanol is a type of alcohol much more potent than that found in ethanol-containing alcoholic beverages. Methanol is known to be neurotoxic and may be the cause of neurological disease and related symptoms that can arise from consumption of aspartame, including headaches, muscle spasms, dizziness, twitching, memory loss, migraines and even seizures.[99]

Neurosurgeon Dr. Russell Blaylock is one of the world's foremost authorities on the biochemistry of aspartame and its effects on brain function. He claims, "Pregnant women should never consume foods containing aspartame. . . . The aspartic acid, phenylalanine, and methanol [components of aspartame] are all known to produce abnormal development of a baby's brain."[100]

While countless studies warn against the harms of sugars and artificial sweeteners, all research points to the many benefits of natural whole grains. When The Green Diet is applied, in a time period as short as two weeks, the unnatural sugars in your body will be purged, and you will realize the benefits of whole grain goodness.

Step 4

Love your World, Protect your World

Baby boomers knowledgeable in the agricultural industry will attest to how different the meat and dairy business is today from the times of their youth. They grew up in an era where cows grazed freely in pasture and people drank raw milk from the milking pail. Today, if you are so lucky as to have access to meat and dairy from a farm where animals are treated humanely, then you comprise a very tiny percent of the population.

The vast majority of meat and dairy people consume today comes from large agribusinesses where the treatment of animals is appalling, and the damage to the environment alarming. Enlightenment into the nature of the agriculture industry is often cause enough for vegetarianism. Here we will break down the negative effects the heavy consumption of animal products has on our world.

Environmental Factors

According to the U.S. Environmental Protection Agency (EPA), chemical and animal waste runoff from factory farms is responsible for more than 173,000 miles of polluted rivers and streams. Runoff from factory farmlands is one of the greatest threats to water quality today. These farms produce huge amounts of animal waste, which is stored in lagoons and often overapplied to surrounding land.

Pizza, p. 107

Manure spills, leaky lagoons, and runoff from oversaturated land carry pollutants in animal waste into surface water and groundwater. This contaminates our public and private water sources, jeopardizing the health and safety of communities that rely upon these supplies for drinking water.[101] Factory farms also greatly deplete our earth's water resources. More than half of all the water consumed in the U.S. is used to raise animals for food. A totally vegetarian diet requires 300 gallons of water per day, while a meat-based diet requires more than 4,000 gallons of water per day.[102]

Ties between animal-oriented agribusiness and global warming are also undeniable. The United Nations' seminal report, "Livestock's Long Shadow," implicated the livestock sector in 18 percent of the world's greenhouse gas emissions.[103] Cattle operations release significant amounts of methane and nitrous oxide. It has been shown that methane is 23 times more warming than carbon dioxide, and nitrous oxide is 296 times more warming.[104]

For those who may argue that a plant-based diet may adversely affect the rainforests, prepare to be surprised. Ironically, eating only plants may help save plants worldwide. Large swaths of rainforests in Central America have been destroyed over the past century in order to make room for cow pastures. So not only does The Green Diet save animals, but it helps save the environment, as well.

The Green Diet's Support of Animal Rights

Many vegetarians give up meat because of their concern for animals. Farmed animals are not protected from cruelty under the law. In fact, the majority of state anti-cruelty laws specifically exempt farm animals from basic humane protection. As more humans become aware of the horrific conditions animals endure in becoming the food we put on our table, we can take action and not only improve our health, but the lives of animals.

Ten billion animals are slaughtered for human consumption each year. In the United States today, most of our meat and dairy come from factory farms. Factory farms are industrial-scale facilities where tens of thousands of animals are crowded together in tight conditions and cannot carry out normal behaviors, such as grazing, rooting, and pecking.[105]

To keep the well over ten billion animals slaughtered every year in the United States alive in unsanitary conditions, factory farms give animals regular doses of antibiotics. Approximately 70 percent of all the antibiotics used in the United States are given to farm animals. These drugs form a toxic residue in the animal's muscle tissues, which is then ingested by consumers.[106] This overuse of antibiotics by factory farms is causing antibiotic-resistant bacterial strains, or "superbugs," to develop, which are immune to the antibiotics.[107] And reportedly, 99 percent of commercially raised cattle are treated with growth hormones.[108]

Dairy cows may suffer worse than cattle raised for meat because of the duration of their suffering. They are continually impregnated and separated from their calves. They are subject to multiple health problems, including mastitis. And in the end, they too are eventually killed for their beef.[109]

The veal industry is notorious for the cruel confinement of calves. Calves are kept in small crates which prevent movement to inhibit muscle growth so their flesh will be tender. They are also fed a diet deficient of iron to keep their flesh pale and appealing to the consumer. Veal calves spend each day confined alone with no companionship, and they are deprived of light for a large portion of their four-month lives.[110]

Pigs are highly social, affectionate, and intelligent creatures, and they suffer both physically and emotionally when they are confined in narrow cages in which they cannot even turn around. With no bedding or soil for them to root in, they often resort to biting other pigs' tails. In response, many factory farms cut off their pigs' tails (taildocking).[111] Pigs are raised inside buildings that have automated water, feed and waste removal. They often don't see daylight until they are shipped for slaughter. Dust, dirt and toxic gases from the pigs' waste further create an unsanitary environment that encourages the onset of a number of diseases and illnesses, including pneumonia, cholera, dysentery and trichinosis."[112]

Broiler chickens are selectively bred and genetically altered to produce bigger thighs and breasts. This breeding creates birds so heavy that their bones cannot support their weight, making it difficult for them to stand. These chickens are raised in overcrowded broiler houses instead of cages to prevent the occurrence of bruised flesh which would make their meat undesirable. Broiler chickens are also often fed arsenic to kill parasites and promote growth. 9 billion chickens are slaughtered every year for people to eat.[113]

In egg factories, birds are held in very small battery cages with slanted wire floors that cause severe discomfort and foot deformation. Between five and eight birds are crammed in cages only fourteen square inches in size. Since the birds have no room to act naturally, they become very aggressive and attack the other birds in their cage. To help combat this behavior, the birds have their beaks seared off at a young age. The chicks are sorted at birth and newborn males are separated and suffocated in trash bags. The remaining layer hens are subjected to constant light to encourage greater egg production. At the end of their laying cycle, they are either slaughtered or forced to molt by water and food deprivation, which shocks them into another layer cycle."[114]

Fish farms, or "aquafarms," can be based on land or in the ocean. Land-based farms raise thousands of fish in ponds, pools, or concrete tanks. Ocean-based farms are situated near shorelines. The fish in these farms are packed into net or mesh cages. Fish farms are rife with pollution and disease.[115] "Conditions on some farms are so horrendous that 30 percent of the fish may die before farmers can kill and package them for food."[116] The massive amount of feces produced by fish on aquafarms is bad for the environment. According to the Norwegian government, the salmon and trout farms in Norway alone produce roughly the same amount of sewage as New York City.[117] Dead fish carcasses and uneaten antibiotic-laden fish feed also pollute the coastal areas that surround these farms. The sludge of fish feces and other debris can be toxic for already-strained ocean ecosystems.

The Green Diet not only positively affects the health of its followers, but also provides numerous benefits to Mother Nature as a whole. There was never a better time to save the environment and support animal rights. Now is the time to go green.

Grilled Skewers with Rosemary-Dijon Vinaigrette, p. 104

Step 5

Total Balance: Here's to a Healthy New You

If you have come this far and are willing to embrace the many positive life changes The Green Diet can provide, you most likely already exercise and avoid substances that can be harmful to your body. But if you'd like a quick refresher course, or perhaps even a kick start to becoming your most healthy self, here are some quick facts to remember.

Exercise

Besides refraining from smoking, exercise is the single best thing you can do to get or stay healthy and keep chronic diseases at bay.[118] Its benefits may seem obvious, but if you are looking for additional motivation to get off the couch, digest this. A report by the U.S. Surgeon General lists the many benefits of frequent exercise as follows: physical activity improves your chances of living longer and staying healthier; helps fight heart disease, high blood pressure and cholesterol; protects you from developing certain cancers; helps prevent type II diabetes; helps prevent arthritis and relieves pain and stiffness in people with arthritis; helps prevent osteoporosis; reduces the risk of falling among older adults; relieves symptoms of depression and anxiety; improves mood and energy levels; helps prevent impotence; and controls weight. If you're not already out for a jog, let's delve deeper.

It is far easier to prevent weight gain than it is to lose it. Gaining weight makes your body more receptive to future weight gain and makes getting rid of extra pounds doubly difficult. Exercise burns calories that would otherwise be stored as fat, while at the same time builds muscle, which constantly burns calories for energy. The more muscle you have, the more calories you burn, even while resting.[119] If you live a sedentary life, your muscles gradually waste away and are replaced by fat, causing your metabolism to decelerate. This shift from muscle to fat makes it easier to gain weight and increases your risk of heart disease and diabetes.[120]

Cardiovascular exercise improves the ability of the heart and blood vessels to supply oxygen to your body so that vital organs perform at peak efficiency. Vigorous exercise also increases circulation, strengthening the heart.[121]

Additionally, physical exercise strengthens bones. When force is applied to a bone, it bends. Apply a large amount of force and the bone may break. Apply a small force and the bend is minuscule but physiologically important, especially when repeated over time. Cells inside the bones respond to physical strain and stress by remodeling the bone to make it stronger and more dense.[122] Among children and young adults, vigorous physical activity sketches the blueprint for the growing skeleton. The more activity and healthy strain on the bones, the more the bones will build. However, too much strain, like heavy weight-lifting, may cause children's growing bones to harden prematurely, stunting growth. During adulthood, exercise helps maintain the balance between bone-building and bone-dissolving processes.[123]

> While vigorous exercise provides the most benefit in terms of improving lipid profile and reducing insulin resistance, even moderate intensity exercise, such as walking, has been shown to reduce cardiovascular risk. In contrast, prolonged sitting increases risk. So make sure you take the stairs!
>
> —Sarah G. Beesley, M.D.

There's no doubt about it: exercise should be a beneficial and essential part of every person's life. When paired with a healthy diet, you can feel confident you are doing your best to guarantee a long and healthy future.

Cleanse Yourself

The Green Diet is a lifestyle plan and, as such, encourages eliminating alcohol, tobacco, tea, and coffee from your life, as all of these products can be extremely addicting and harmful to your system. Breaking from these habits will bring you freedom and control over your daily choices and your future.

One of the most harmful substances to your health is tobacco. Smoking has been implicated as a strong risk factor for a number of diseases. Besides lung, stomach, pancreatic and bladder cancer, smoking increases the risk of heart and vascular disease, as well as lung diseases such as chronic bronchitis and emphysema. Smoking also increases the risk of premature birth and infant mortality. Quitting smoking is one of the best things anyone can do for his or her health. But as tobacco is extremely addictive, seek help from your doctor or other social support for assistance when quitting the habit.

Another substance The Green Diet advocates avoiding is alcohol. While wine in limited quantities has been shown to have a possible benefit on reducing cardiovascular risk, this benefit may also be gained by just drinking red grape juice. It is very difficult for most people to restrict themselves to the small amount of alcohol that has been shown to be beneficial. And after exceeding that limit, alcohol has many harmful effects. In the short-term, substantial harm to self or others may occur through careless behavior while intoxicated, especially if driving is involved. Over many years, alcohol greatly increases the risk of liver disease, several different types of cancer, and pancreatic disease. Alcohol can also have serious effects on interpersonal relationships and families.

Many people turn to coffee and tea for the energy boost their caffeine can provide. However, many studies have shown that caffeine can have negative effects on the body. Caffeine increases the levels of adenosine, cortisol, and dopamine in your body, causing short-term perceived benefits (but long-term negative effects such as fatigue, moodiness, and irritability). Coffee and non-herbal teas also contain many substances such as tannin, thein, cynogen, stricknein, cyanide and aeromic oil, all of which can be harmful when taken in excessive amounts.

While strategic marketing campaigns would have you believe you need to pay big bucks to be happy, energetic, and productive, Mother Nature actually provides your body all of the positive energy it needs through its nutrient-rich, plant-based foods. When looking for a "pick-me-up," turning to healthy foods and exercise is the best way to achieve a natural high.

Step 6

Easy to Make, Delicious to Eat: Recipes and Weekly Menu Planning

Adapting The Green Diet into your life does not require a revolutionary endeavor in the kitchen each day. A green meal can be as familiar as spaghetti, as comforting as a bowl of smooth tomato soup, or as exotic as baked leek and sweet potato gratin. Most people—whether plant eaters or meat eaters—typically rotate through a limited variety of recipes. In fact, the average family eats only eight or nine different dinners repeatedly.[124] So by taking the time in advance to select a handful or two of recipes that sound appealing to you, you can avoid the "What's for dinner?" drudgery and instead look forward to your healthy, tasty meals.

To turn your weekly menu plan green, you can start with a simple three-step method. First, think of two to three vegetarian meals that you already enjoy. Meals like minestrone, vegetable stir-fry, and pasta primavera are good examples. Secondly, think of three recipes that you prepare regularly that can easily be adapted to The Green Diet with only a few changes. Perhaps a favorite chili recipe can be made with all the same ingredients if you replace the meat with beans or texturized vegetable protein. Bean burritos instead of beef burritos and veggie burgers instead of hamburgers are other good substitutions. Many soups, stews, pastas, and casseroles also can be made into vegetarian dishes with a few simple changes. Also, remember to swap all refined carbohydrates with whole grain products. And third, discover the recipes in this book. Test the ones that appeal to you until you find at least three or four that you love and are easy for you to make. Then, *voila!* With only a little planning and a few simple changes to your usual dining fare, you will have nine great, green meals.

Helpful Hints for Green Dieters

It's Time to Get Acquainted with Your Local Health Foods Store

Exploring your hometown health food store can be a fun and rewarding experience, as you will see that many foods easily fit into your Green Diet. I love to experiment with the different grains and beans I find. I often discover delicious dry bean soup mixes in the bulk sections of my local Henry's or Mother's Market. I also love to stock up on unsweetened dried fruit and various nuts so I always have a healthy treat to snack on. Chia seeds and flax seeds make a great addition to fruit smoothies, salads, breads, and many other dishes. Nutritional yeast is a protein and vitamin B-rich food with a cheesy/nutty flavor that is great to sprinkle on salads, popcorn, pasta, and much more. As you browse the aisles of your local market, you will find many new Green Diet-approved tastes to discover. Have fun trying them out!

When Dining around Town

Strive to follow your Green Diet eating plan no matter where you eat, even in restaurants or at social events. Before going out, assess your hunger level; and, if you are very hungry, have a small snack before leaving so you can make sure that you are in control when ordering. Always be prepared to articulate special requests to your server, while keeping in mind that restaurants aim to please you and will usually modify a menu item per request. Vegetarian items are frequently found on most menus and are even offered on airplanes and at most social events.

To avoid consuming animal products, ask that all your items be prepared without butter, milk, or cheese. Many restaurants will also offer "healthy heart" alternatives like brown rice or whole wheat pastas. If you are having a hard time selecting an appetizing meal, you can always order an extra large salad with the dressing on the side. And if dairy-free dressing is not available, sprinkle your salad with lemon juice or vinegar and a touch of olive oil. To top it all off, a good dessert choice is fresh fruit—just hold the sugar and cream.

Mom's Salad Bar

Over time, my mom has migrated toward eating salads all the time. She loves them! There are days when she will eat a salad for every meal. She claims they fill her up and keep her satisfied right up until her next meal. Her favorite lunch is a salad with a cup of one of her easy pea, carrot, or cauliflower soups (see recipe section) and a slice of whole grain bread.

For simple salad preparation, I recommend starting with a bed of greens and then adding a fruit, a nut, and at least one vegetable. To add a little more flavor, you can add dressing if you like, but watch out for the hidden sugars and chemicals in store-bought dressings. My mom mixes up different oil and vinegar dressings and keeps them on hand in the fridge, ready to go. Her favorite is the Sweet Dijon Vinaigrette.

To prepare nuts for a salad, you can chop them up and toast them in a dry pan over medium heat until they are slightly toasted. My mom then likes to sprinkle them with salt and pepper, and she sometimes adds a drizzle of honey for a sweet crunchy glaze.

The great thing about salads is that you can experiment with different salad combinations all the time. Here are some of my mom's tried-and-true favorites.

- Pears, blueberries, and pecans over baby romaine
- Oranges, avocado, jicama, and pine nuts over any mild greens
- Fresh berries, apple, red onion, and walnut over mache
- Sunflower seeds with white mushrooms and flaxseeds over any mild greens
- Grated carrots, peas, beets, raisins, and sunflower seeds over baby romaine

- Strawberries, almonds, poppy seeds, mushrooms, and sliced red onion over spinach

Egg Substitutions

The next time you prepare a recipe that calls for eggs, try one of these simple substitutes:

- If a recipe calls for just one or two eggs, you can often skip them and add two tablespoons of water per egg to balance out the moisture content.

- Use powdered (eggless) egg replacers that can be found at most natural food stores.

- Mix one heaping tablespoon of soy flour or cornstarch with two tablespoons water to replace each egg in a baked product.

- One ounce of mashed tofu can replace one egg. Scramble crumbled tofu with onions and peppers seasoned with cumin and curry to replace eggs in breakfast dishes.

- In muffins and cookies, half of a banana can be used instead of an egg, although it will affect the flavor somewhat.

- For veggie loaves and burgers, tomato paste, mashed potatoes, moistened bread crumbs, or rolled oats are good binders in lieu of eggs.

- Two tablespoons of finely ground flax seeds mixed with three tablespoons water substitutes for one egg. Let the mixture sit a couple of minutes until it become like jelly, then add as you would eggs.

- One tablespoon of tapioca or cornstarch, one tablespoon potato starch, one-fourth teaspoon baking powder and one-eighth teaspoon xanthan gum (if you have it) mixed with a half cup water and two teaspoons oil will replace two whole eggs. This works well in delicate recipes.

Dairy-Free Substitutions

- Top your oats or cereal with fortified rice or almond milk.

- Make smoothies with enriched soymilk or soy yogurt.

- Order your meals with no cheese. Ask for guacamole, brown rice, or extra salsa in your burrito instead of cheese. Add more vegetables, beans, nuts, or baked tofu chunks instead of cheese to a salad.

- Use plain soymilk in soups and savory dishes.

- Make creamy dips and desserts using silken tofu in place of sour cream or cream cheese.

- Sprinkle nutritional yeast on popcorn or pasta for a cheesy flavor, instead of parmesan.

You now have all the tools required to embrace The Green Diet! Congratulations for taking the time to explore the way of eating that Mother Nature intended for you. May you enjoy all of the health and lifestyle benefits that will bless your body and soul as you go green.

Fruit and Spicy Nut Trail Mix, p. 164

Recipes

Pineapple and Watermelon, p. 159

Appetizers and Dips

Almond "Feta" Cheese with Herb Oil, p. 57

Almond "Feta" Cheese with Herb Oil

Blanched almonds give this creamy-crumbly cheese a rich texture. Unbaked, it will be smooth and spreadable. Baking will make it a bit more crumbly, like traditional feta cheese.

> 1 cup whole blanched almonds
> 1/4 cup lemon juice
> 3 Tbs plus 1/4 cup olive oil, divided
> 1 clove garlic
> 1 1/4 Tbs salt
> 1 Tbs fresh thyme
> 1 tsp fresh rosemary

1   Place almonds in medium bowl, and cover with 3 inches cold water. Let soak 24 hours. Drain soaking liquid, rinse almonds under cold running water, and drain again.

2   Purée almonds, lemon juice, 3 Tbs oil, garlic, salt, and 1/2 cup cold water in food processor 6 minutes, or until very smooth and creamy.

3   Place large strainer over bowl, and line with triple layer of cheesecloth. (Paper towels will work if you don't have cheesecloth.) Spoon almond mixture into cheesecloth. Bring corners and sides of cloth together, and twist around cheese, forming into an orange-sized ball and squeezing to help extract moisture. Secure with rubber band or kitchen twine. Chill 12 hours, or overnight. Discard excess liquid.

4   Preheat oven to 200° F. Line baking sheet with parchment paper. Unwrap "cheese" (it will be soft), and transfer from cheesecloth to prepared baking sheet. Flatten to form 6-inch round about 3/4-inch thick. Bake 40 minutes, or until top

is slightly firm. Cool, then chill. (Cheese can be made up to this point 2 days ahead; keep refrigerated.)

5   Combine remaining 1/4 cup oil, thyme, and rosemary in small saucepan. Warm oil over medium-low heat 2 minutes, or until very hot but not simmering. Cool to room temperature. Drizzle herb oil over cheese just before serving.

Servings: 10

Nutrition (per serving): 132 calories, 12.7g total fat, 3.4g carbohydrates, 1.7g fiber, <1g sugar, 3.1g protein, 14.8IU vitamin a, 3.3mg vitamin c, 39.1mg calcium, <1mg iron, <1mg vitamin b6, 5.5mcg folate, 291.1mg sodium, 113.8mg potassium.

Avocado and Corn Dip

2 ripe Hass avocados, peeled and pitted
2 tsp lime juice
1 Tbs finely chopped cilantro
salt and pepper
1 cup store-bought salsa
1/2 cup canned black beans, rinsed and drained
1/2 cup frozen corn, thawed
2 scallions, chopped
dash of hot sauce, to taste
tortilla chips

1 Place the avocado in a bowl. Mash with a fork and add the lime juice and chopped cilantro. Season with salt and pepper. Stir well.

2 Add the salsa, black beans, corn, scallions, and hot sauce; season with salt and pepper. Mix well.

3 Enjoy with tortilla chips.

Servings: 4

Nutrition (per serving): 132 calories, 12.7g total fat, 3.4g carbohydrates, 1.7g fiber, <1g sugar, 3.1g protein, 14.8IU vitamin a, 3.3mg vitamin c, 39.1mg calcium, <1mg iron, <1mg vitamin b6, 5.5mcg folate, 291.1mg sodium, 113.8mg potassium.

Chunky Guacamole Dip

3 avocados
1 medium tomato, diced
1/2 tsp garlic, minced
juice of 1 lime
1 tsp salt, or to taste
1/2 tsp pepper
1 tsp extra virgin olive oil
1/4 cup finely chopped red onion

1   Pit and peel the avocado, cut into 1/2-inch cubes. Put avocados in medium mixing bowl and pour the juice of 1 lime over the top. Mix so that the juice coats all the avocado pieces.

2   Add the remaining ingredients. Mix well. Serve immediately or store covered with an airtight seal or plastic wrap.

Servings: 6

Nutrition (per serving): 158 calories, 14.1g total fat, 9g carbohydrates, 6.3g fiber, <1g sugar, 2g protein, 298.4IU vitamin a, 10.3mg vitamin c, 15.9mg calcium, <1mg iron, <1mg vitamin b6, 80.1mcg folate, 395.8mg sodium, 490.4mg potassium.

Grilled Vegetable Antipasto Platter

6 baby artichokes
4 large portobello mushrooms, about 5 oz each,
   cleaned with stems removed
3 Tbs extra virgin olive oil
2 Tbs lemon juice (1/2 a lemon)
2 tsp balsamic vinegar
kosher salt and freshly ground black pepper
1 large red bell pepper
1 bunch arugula

1 Bring a saucepan 3/4 full of water to a boil. While the water is heating, using a sharp knife, slice off the top 1/2 inch of the leaves of each artichoke. Starting at the base, pull off and discard the tough outer leaves until you reach the pale inner leaves. Cut off all but 1/2 inch of the stem and peel its tough outside flesh.

2 Add the artichokes to the boiling water, reduce the heat so that the water is at a gentle boil, cover, and cook until a knife inserted just above the base meets only slight resistance, about 15 minutes. Drain well. Cut each artichoke in quarters lengthwise. Scoop out and discard any prickly chokes. Set aside.

3 Prepare grill for direct-heat grilling over medium high heat. Oil the grill rack, the artichoke quarters, and the portobello mushroom caps.

4   In a bowl, whisk together the lemon juice, vinegar, and olive oil until blended. Stir in 1/4 tsp salt and season with pepper. Set aside.

5   Place the bell pepper over the hottest part of the grill, turning as needed until the skin is blistered and charred black on all sides, 6–8 minutes. Transfer to a paper bag, close loosely, and let steam for about 15 minutes.

6   Place the artichoke quarters with cut side down on grill until grill marks are visible, about 2 minutes. Repeat on the other cut side. Remove to a plate.

7   Grill the mushrooms gill side up for 3 minutes, rotate 90°, then grill another 2 minutes. Flip and grill for another minute, until the center is tender. Transfer to the plate with the artichokes.

8   Remove the bell pepper from the bag, and peel away the charred skin. Seed the pepper and cut into strips.

9   Cover the platter with a bed of arugula. Arrange the artichokes, mushrooms, and bell pepper on the greens. Stir the vinaigrette and pour over vegetables. Serve at once.

Servings: 6

Nutrition (per serving): 148 calories, 7.3g total fat, 19.1g carbohydrates, 7.7g fiber, 4.3g sugar, 6.6g protein, 1192IU vitamin a, 65.3mg vitamin c, 66.7mg calcium, 2.2mg iron, <1mg vit. b6, 86.6mcg folate, 387.1mg sodium, 963.2mg potassium.

Pomodori Al Forno (Baked Tomatoes)

1 cup extra virgin olive oil (or more)
2 pounds plum tomatoes, halved lengthwise
1 1/2 tsp dried oregano
1 tsp agave nectar
1/2 tsp salt
1–2 cloves garlic, minced
2 tsp minced fresh parsley
1 whole wheat baguette, thinly sliced
crosswise and toasted

1 Preheat oven to 250° F. Pour 1/2 cup oil into a 13 x 9 x 2-inch glass or ceramic baking dish. Arrange tomatoes in dish, cut side up. Drizzle with remaining 1/2 cup oil. Sprinkle with oregano, sugar, and salt. Bake 1 hour. Using tongs, turn tomatoes over. Bake 1 hour longer. Turn tomatoes over again. Bake until deep red and very tender, transferring tomatoes to plate when soft (time will vary, depending on ripeness of tomatoes), about 15 to 45 minutes longer.

2 Layer tomatoes in medium bowl, sprinkling garlic and parsley over each layer; reserve oil in baking dish. Drizzle tomatoes with reserved oil. Let stand at room temperature for 2 hours. (At this point, you can cover and chill up to 5 days. Bring to room temperature before serving.)

3 Serve with toasted whole wheat baguette slices.

Servings: 10

Nutrition (per serving): 240 calories, 12.5g total fat, 28.1g carbohydrates, 2.4g fiber, <1g sugar, 4.7g protein, 535IU vitamin a, 21.3mg vitamin c, 42.7mg calcium, 1.7mg iron, <1mg vit. b6, 27.1mcg folate, 400.3mg sodium, 235.7mg potassium.

Queso Fake-Out Dip

When I first made this, my family thought it was cheesy queso dip. It's delicious. Serve with corn chips.

1 can (15 oz) cannellini beans, rinsed and drained
1 Tbs extra virgin olive oil
1 clove garlic, minced
2 Tbs fresh lime juice
3 Tbs sun-dried tomato pieces (4–5 pieces), packed in oil
1/4 cup water, or as needed
coarse salt

1   Place the beans, oil, garlic, lime juice, and tomatoes in a food processor and process until the mixture resembles coarse meal. Slowly add a bit of the water and process into a smooth paste (if mixture is too thick, add more water). Taste for seasoning and add salt, if desired.

Servings: 8

Nutrition (per serving): 105 calories, 2.2g total fat, 16.2g carbohydrates, 4g fiber, <1g sugar, 6.1g protein, 30.7IU vitamin a, 3.5mg vitamin c, 63mg calcium, 2.7mg iron, <1mg vitamin b6, <1mcg folate, 29.7mg sodium, 494.2mg potassium.

Red Bean Dip with Pita

1 cup dried pinto beans, soaked in water
  overnight and drained
1 1/2 tsp salt
1 small red onion
1 tsp ground cumin
1/2 tsp dried oregano
1/8 tsp chipotle chili powder
1/4 cup tomato sauce
1/4 cup firmly packed fresh cilantro
kosher salt and freshly ground black pepper
2 pita breads

1 Place soaked, drained beans in a saucepan and add salt and water to cover generously. Bring to a boil over high heat, reduce the heat to low, cover partially, and simmer gently until very soft, 1–1 1/2 hours. Drain well and set aside to cool.

2 Chop the onion and place in a food processor with the beans, cumin, oregano, chile powder, tomato sauce, and cilantro. Process until smooth. Add a bit of the bean cooking liquid if dip is too thick. Pour into a bowl and stir in 1/2 tsp salt, or more to taste. Season with pepper.

3 Preheat the oven to 400° F. Lightly brush one side of the pita breads with olive oil and place on a baking sheet. Bake until crisp, 6–8 minutes. Remove and transfer the pita breads to a wire rack to cool.

4 Place the bowl of dip on a platter, arrange the pita wedges around the bowl, and serve.

Servings: 8

Nutrition (per serving): 102 calories, <1g total fat, 18.4g carbohydrates, 4.4g fiber, <1g sugar, 5.8g protein, 136.6IU vit. a, 2.7mg vitamin c, 35.4mg calcium, 1.7mg iron, <1mg vit. b6, 129.8mcg folate, 534.8mg sodium, 381.8mg potassium.

Scallion and Roasted Pine Nut Hummus

3 Tbs pine nuts
1 can (15 oz) chickpeas
1/2 cup sliced green onions, divided
1–2 cloves garlic, minced
2–3 Tbs fresh lemon juice
1/2 tsp ground cumin
1 Tbs extra virgin olive oil
salt, to taste

1   Toast the pine nuts in a small skillet over medium-low heat until lightly brown. Stir frequently.

2   Drain and rinse the chickpeas. Put the chickpeas, 1/4 cup green onions and remaining ingredients in a food processor until smooth. Add water if needed to get desired consistency. Check seasoning and add salt as needed.

3   Stir in the remaining green onions and the pine nuts. Serve at room temperature.

4   Serve with whole wheat pita bread or raw vegetables.

Servings: 10

Nutrition (per serving): 70 calories, 3.5g total fat, 8.2g carbohydrates, 1.6g fiber, <1g sugar, 2g protein, 60IU vitamin a, 3.7mg vitamin c, 15.8mg calcium, <1mg iron, <1mg vitamin b6, 25.4mcg folate, 109.9mg sodium, 89.8mg potassium.

Simple Bruschetta

1 whole wheat baguette, sliced diagonally into 24 slices
5 medium tomatoes, chopped
1/2 cup basil, chopped
1 clove garlic, minced
1/4 cup extra virgin olive oil
1/2 tsp balsamic vinegar
salt and freshly ground black pepper, to taste

1   Preheat the oven to 350° F. Lay baguette slices in a single layer on a baking sheet and bake for 10 minutes or until golden.

2   Meanwhile, mix chopped tomatoes, basil, garlic, olive oil, balsamic vinegar, and salt and pepper in a small bowl.

3   Top each piece of toast with a spoonful of the tomato and basil mixture.

Servings: 12

Nutrition (per serving): 165 calories, 7.2g total fat, 21.5g carbohydrates, 1.7g fiber, 1.1g sugar, 3.8g protein, 434.7IU vitamin a, 5.7mg vitamin c, 36.1mg calcium, 1.2mg iron, <1mg vit. b6, 19mcg folate, 232.6mg sodium, 150.1mg potassium.

Spiced Pita Chips

2 Tbs extra virgin olive oil
1 tsp ground cumin
1/2 tsp ground coriander
1/4 tsp cayenne pepper
1/2 tsp garlic powder
1/4 tsp fresh ground black pepper
1/4 tsp salt
3 whole wheat pitas, each pita cut into 8 triangles

1   Preheat oven to 350° F. Combine olive oil and all spices in a large bowl. Add pita wedges and toss to coat.

2   Spread in 1 layer on a baking sheet and bake for about 15 minutes, tossing once, or until pita is brown and crisp. Cool completely before serving.

Servings: 6

Nutrition (per serving): 61 calories, 4.8g total fat, 4.4g carbohydrates, <1g fiber, <1g sugar, <1g protein, 35.9IU vitamin a, <1mg vitamin c, 6.2mg calcium, <1mg iron, <1mg vitamin b6, 2.6mcg folate, 135mg sodium, 25.3mg potassium.

Spinach and Cannellini Bean Dip

2 Tbs extra virgin olive oil
2 cloves garlic
12 oz fresh baby spinach
15 oz canned cannelloni beans, rinsed and drained
1 Tbs fresh lemon juice
1 Tbs balsamic vinegar
1 tsp kosher salt
1/4 tsp black pepper

1. In a large nonstick skillet, heat 1 tablespoon of the oil over medium heat. Add the garlic and cook until fragrant, about 1 minute. Add the spinach and cook for 2 minutes until wilted. Let the mixture cool for a few minutes.

2. Place the remaining olive oil, spinach mixture, cannelloni beans, lemon juice, balsamic vinegar, salt, and pepper in the bowl of a food processor.

3. Blend until the mixture is smooth. Transfer to a small serving bowl. Serve with endive spears, toast or pita chips.

Servings: 6

Nutrition (per serving): 292 calories, 5.3g total fat, 45.5g carbohydrates, 12.1g fiber, <1g sugar, 18.3g protein, 5317.5IU vit. a, 17.4mg vit. c, 228.8mg calcium, 9mg iron, <1mg vit. b6, 110.4mcg folate, 369.9mg sodium, 1599.7mg potassium.

Strawberry Banana Smoothie, p. 74

Beverages

Banana, Strawberry, Peach Smoothie

1 1/2 very ripe bananas, peeled and frozen
4–6 strawberries, hulled and frozen, plus 2 for garnish
1/2 peach, pitted, plus 2 slices for garnish
3/4 cup peach nectar

1. Select 2 tumblers. In a blender, combine the bananas, the 4 to 6 strawberries, the peach, and peach nectar. Process until thick and creamy. Divide between the glasses.

2. Garnish each glass with a peach slice and a strawberry and serve immediately. Serves 2.

Servings: 2

Variations

Banana, strawberry, and mango: Replace peach with 1/2 mango and swap the peach nectar for mango juice.

Banana kiwi: Substitute 1 cup frozen kiwi cubes for the strawberries and peach. Replace peach nectar with 1/2 cup coconut milk.

Nutrition (per serving): 156 calories, <1g total fat, 39.7g carbohydrates, 4.3g fiber, 15.4g sugar, 1.8g protein, 383.9IU vitamin a, 66.1mg vitamin c, 19.2mg calcium, <1mg iron, <1mg vitamin b6, 32.6mcg folate, 8mg sodium, 483.4mg potassium.

Stomach-Soothing Papaya Smoothie

Papaya is known for its soothing effect on upset digestive systems. Ginger can help ease motion sickness. If you don't like the taste of fresh ginger, simply leave it out.

1 cup cubed ripe papaya
6 frozen strawberries
1/2 cup plain soymilk
1 Tbs lime juice
1 tsp agave nectar or honey
1/4 tsp grated fresh ginger

1   Puree all ingredients in blender until smooth.

Servings: 1

Nutrition (per serving): 166 calories, 2.4g total fat, 33g carbohydrates, 5g fiber, 22g sugar, 5.3g protein, 1823.6IU vitamin a, 141.6mg vitamin c, 234mg calcium, 1.6mg iron, <1mg vit. b6, 72.3mcg folate, 53.9mg sodium, 621.2mg potassium.

Strawberry Banana Smoothie

6 medium frozen strawberries
1 medium ripe banana
1/4 cup orange juice
1/2 cup vanilla soy yogurt

1   Blend together in a blender until smooth.

Servings: 1

Nutrition (per serving): 310 calories, 2.6g total fat, 68.8g carbohydrates, 5.6g fiber, 43.8g sugar, 8.8g protein, 314.8IU vitamin a, 92.6mg vitamin c, 250.4mg calcium, 1.1mg iron, <1mg vit. b6, 61mcg folate, 89.1mg sodium, 957.8mg potassium.

Breakfast and Bread

Apricot Nut Bread, p. 77

Apricot Nut Bread

1 cup apple juice
1/2 cup all-fruit apricot spread or jam
2/3 cup dried apricot pieces
1/2 cup oat bran
1/3 cup canola oil
2 medium ripe bananas, mashed
2 Tbs honey
2 cups whole wheat flour
1 tsp baking powder
1 tsp cinnamon
1/4 tsp coarse salt
1/4 cup chopped walnuts (or other nut)

1 Preheat the oven to 350° F. Bring the apple juice to a boil in a small saucepan. Remove from heat and add the apricot spread, apricots, and oat bran. Let stand for 5 minutes.

2 Combine the oil, bananas, and honey in a large mixing bowl; whisk well. Add apricot mixture. Add the dry ingredients to the banana-apricot mixture, stirring just until moist.

3 Spoon the batter into a greased loaf pan. Bake for 55–65 minutes or until pick inserted into the center comes out clean. Cool and enjoy.

Servings: 12

Nutrition (per serving): 230 calories, 8.4g total fat, 39.2g carbohydrates, 4.3g fiber, 16.7g sugar, 4.3g protein, 220.1IU vitamin a, 11.6mg vitamin c, 44.3mg calcium, 1.5mg iron, <1mg vit. b6, 22.1mcg folate, 97.2mg sodium, 279.2mg potassium.

Basic Healthy Granola

2 tsp canola oil
1 1/4 cups regular rolled oats
1/8 cup flax meal
1 tsp cinnamon
pinch of salt
1/4 cup apple juice
2 Tbs maple syrup
2 Tbs honey

1 Preheat oven to 325° F. Lightly grease baking sheet with canola oil (you may also use cooking-oil spray or line baking sheet with nonstick foil). In a medium bowl, combine the oats, flax meal, cinnamon, and salt. Mix well. In a small bowl combine the apple juice, maple syrup, and honey. Mix well.

2 Add the wet ingredients to the dry ingredients, stirring until the mixture is fully combined and moist. Spread the mixture on the greased baking sheet and bake for 15 minutes.

3 Remove from the oven and stir, breaking the large chunks into smaller pieces. Bake for an additional 8 minutes or until crisp. Remove from oven and allow to cool. While still warm, stir to break up any remaining chunks. When completely cool, store the granola in an airtight container.

Servings: 3

Nutrition (per serving): 250 calories, 4.4g total fat, 48.3g carbohydrates, 5.6g fiber, 20g sugar, 6.7g protein, 2.4IU vitamin a, 9mg vitamin c, 51.1mg calcium, 2.4mg iron, <1mg vitamin b6, 29.3mcg folate, 57.8mg sodium, 225mg potassium.

Carrot and Wheat Germ Muffins

2 cups whole wheat flour
1 cup toasted wheat germ
1 Tbs baking powder
1/2 tsp coarse salt
6 Tbs water
4 Tbs flax meal
2 Tbs canola oil
1 cup apple juice
1/2 cup frozen unsweetened apple juice
   concentrate, thawed
1/3 cup unsweetened applesauce
1 cup grated carrots
1/2 cup golden raisins
1/3 cup chopped walnuts

1 Preheat oven to 375° F. Mix the flax meal and the water until well-combined. Set aside for a couple of minutes until it forms a loose jelly.

2 Combine the first four ingredients in a small mixing bowl; whisk well.

3 Combine the flax meal jelly and the next four ingredients in a large mixing bowl; beat well at medium speed of a mixer. Add the dry ingredients, stirring just until moist. Fold in carrots, raisins, and walnuts; spoon the batter into muffin cups lightly coated with cooking spray or oil, filling the cups about 2/3 full. Bake at 375° F for 25–30 minutes or until a wooden pick inserted in the center comes out clean. Cool and enjoy.

Servings: 14

Nutrition (per serving): 183 calories, 6.2g total fat, 29.2g carbohydrates, 4.8g fiber, 3.6g sugar, 5.7g protein, 949.7IU vitamin a, 16mg vitamin c, 84.9mg calcium, 1.8mg iron, <1mg vit. b6, 44.7mcg folate, 199.3mg sodium, 301.5mg potassium.

Flaxseed Boule, p. 81

Flaxseed Boule

1 cup plus 1 Tbs flaxseeds
3 Tbs honey
1 1/2 Tbs active dry yeast
5 cups whole wheat flour
2 tsp salt

1 Place 1/2 cup flaxseeds in bowl, and cover with 3 inches water. Let soak overnight.

2 Combine the honey, yeast, and 2 cups warm water. Let stand 5 minutes or until yeast becomes foamy and fragrant. (If the mixture fails to proof, your yeast may be old.) Grind remaining 1/2 cup plus 1 tablespoon flaxseeds in a coffee grinder or grain mill. Stir together ground flaxseed, whole wheat flour, and salt in a large bowl. Drain soaked flaxseeds; the mixture will be thick and goopy.

3 Using a stand mixer with a dough hook or by hand, combine the yeast mixture, flaxseeds, and flour mixture together until a smooth dough forms. Knead dough 7–10 minutes, or until dough is smooth and no longer sticks to your fingers or the side of mixer; you may need to add some flour as you knead. Shape into a ball and place into a large bowl coated with oil. Cover and let rise in a warm place 1 to 1 1/2 hours, or until doubled in size. Punch down and divide into 2 equal parts. Reshape into 2 balls and cover. Let rise 1 hour more.

4 Preheat oven to 400° F, and coat large baking sheet with oil or cooking spray. Shape each ball of dough into a tight ball, and place on prepared baking sheet, at least 10 inches apart. Brush dough balls with water, and sprinkle with flaxseeds. Bake 40–60 minutes or until loaf is dark brown and sounds hollow when tapped. Cool 15 minutes before slicing.

Servings: 24

Nutrition (per serving): 136 calories, 2.5g total fat, 24.4g carbohydrates, 2.6g fiber, 2.3g sugar, 4.2g protein, <1IU vitamin a, <1mg vitamin c, 17.4mg calcium, 1.7mg iron, <1mg vitamin b6, 77.4mcg folate, 196.9mg sodium, 83.3mg potassium.

Granola with Cashews, Dried Fruit, and Wheat Germ

1 cup regular rolled oats
1/4 cup wheat germ
1/4 cup shredded unsweetened coconut
1/4 cup chopped cashews
1/4 cup chopped walnuts
1 Tbs sesame seeds
1/4 cup pure maple syrup
2 Tbs canola oil
2 Tbs honey
1 Tbs mild-flavored (light) molasses
1/2 tsp ground cinnamon
1/4 cup raisins
1/4 cup chopped dried apricots

1 Preheat oven to 350° F. Mix first 6 ingredients in large bowl. Whisk maple syrup and next 4 ingredients in medium bowl. Add wet ingredients to dry ingredients; stir to coat evenly. Transfer to greased, large-rimmed baking sheet, spreading out in even layer.

2 Bake 12 minutes, then stir. Bake until gloden brown, about 12 minutes longer. Mix in raisins and apricots. Bake until fruit is heated though and granola is slightly darker, about 8 more minutes. Cool completely on sheet. Transfer to airtight container.

Can be made 1 week ahead. Store at room temperature.

Servings: 6

Nutrition (per serving): 333 calories, 18.3g total fat, 40.6g carbohydrates, 4.8g fiber, 22.5g sugar, 6.1g protein, 134.5IU vitamin a, <1mg vitamin c, 56.1mg calcium, 2.5mg iron, <1mg vit. b6, 26.9mcg folate, 9.3mg sodium, 369.8mg potassium.

Hearty Wheat Berry and Oat Groat Bread

2 Tbs sunflower seeds
2 Tbs wheat berries
2 Tbs steel cut oats
2 tsp active dry yeast
1 1/4 cups warm water (105°–115°)
2 Tbs molasses
1 1/2 tsp coarse salt
2 Tbs canola oil
2 1/2–3 cups whole wheat flour

1   Place the first 3 ingredients in a non-stick skillet over medium heat and roast for 3–6 minutes or until lightly brown, stirring frequently.

2   Combine the yeast and 1/2 cup warm water in a large bowl; let stand 5 minutes to proof. Make sure that the yeast is active before continuing. Stir in molasses, salt, and oil. Add 2 1/2 cups wheat flour; stir to form a soft dough. Turn the dough out onto a lightly floured surface and knead until smooth and elastic (6–8 minutes). Add enough of the remaining flour, 1 Tbs at a time, to prevent the dough from sticking to your hands. Knead the seeds, wheat berries, and oat groats into the dough until well dispersed, 1–2 minutes. (This bread can be made in a mixer with a dough hook on low speed.)

3   Place the dough in a large bowl lightly coated with oil, turning to coat the top. Cover and let rise in a warm place (85° F), free from drafts, 1–2 hours or until doubled in size. Punch the dough down, then turn out onto a lightly floured

surface and roll the dough into a 12 x 7-inch rectangle. Roll up the rectangle tightly, starting with the short end; press firmly to eliminate air pockets, and pinch the seam and ends to seal. Place the roll, seam side down, in a greased non-stick loaf pan. Cover and let rise until the dough reaches the top of the pan, 50–60 minutes. Bake at 350° for 45 minutes or until the loaf sounds hollow when tapped. Remove from pan immediately and cool on a wire rack.

Servings: 12

Nutrition (per serving): 135 calories, 3.6g total fat, 23.1g carbohydrates, 3.8g fiber, 2g sugar, 4.7g protein, 2.6IU vitamin a, <1mg vitamin c, 18.8mg calcium, 1.6mg iron, <1mg vitamin b6, 61.7mcg folate, 300.2mg sodium, 208.7mg potassium.

Mango, Banana, and Macadamia Nut Granola

2 tsp canola oil
1 1/4 cups regular rolled oats
1/8 cup flax meal
1 tsp cinnamon
1/4 cup apple juice
2 Tbs maple syrup
2 Tbs honey
1/8 cup macadamia nuts, peeled and chopped
2 Tbs unsalted, dry-roasted soy-nut halves
1/8 tsp grated fresh ginger root
2 Tbs light coconut milk
1 tsp vanilla extract
1 cup chopped dried mango
1/3 cup chopped banana chips

1   Preheat oven to 325° F. Lightly grease baking sheet with canola oil (you may also use cooking-oil spray or line baking sheet with nonstick foil). In a medium bowl, combine the oats, flax meal, macadamia nuts, soy nuts, ginger, cinnamon, and a pinch of salt. Mix well. In a small bowl, combine the apple juice, maple syrup, honey, coconut milk and vanilla extract. Mix well.

2   Add the wet ingredients to the dry ingredients, stirring until the mixture is fully combined and moist. Spread the mixture on the greased baking sheet and bake for 15 minutes.

3   Remove from the oven and stir, breaking the large chunks into smaller pieces. Add the dried mango and banana chips. Bake for an additional 8 minutes or until crisp. Remove

from oven and allow to cool. While still warm, stir to break up any remaining chunks. When completely cool, store the granola in an airtight container.

Servings: 6

Nutrition (per serving): 225 calories, 8.9g total fat, 33.4g carbohydrates, 4.5g fiber, 16g sugar, 5.2g protein, 222.6IU vitamin a, 12.5mg vitamin c, 37mg calcium, 1.6mg iron, <1mg vit. b6, 27.4mcg folate, 30.4mg sodium, 250.4mg potassium.

Moist Banana Blueberry Pancakes

2 cups whole wheat flour
2 tsp baking powder
1/2 tsp salt
1/4 tsp ground cinnamon
1/8 tsp ground allspice
2 cups soy milk
2 Tbs maple syrup, plus more for serving
3 medium bananas
1/2 cup applesauce
2 cups blueberries

1   In a large bowl, combine the flour, sugar, baking powder, salt, cinnamon, and allspice. Set aside.

2   Mash well two of the bananas and mix with the soy milk; stir in maple syrup and applesauce. Pour the wet ingredients into the dry ingredients, mixing with a few swift strokes until just combined. Chop the remaining bananas. Fold bananas and blueberries in until just mixed.

3   Heat a lightly oiled griddle or skillet over medium heat. Cook pancakes and serve with maple syrup.

Servings: 6

Nutrition (per serving): 274 calories, 1.4g total fat, 61.1g carbohydrates, 4.5g fiber, 16.3g sugar, 6.4g protein, 140.8IU vitamin a, 14.1mg vitamin c, 167.2mg calcium, 3mg iron, <1mg vit. b6, 94.7mcg folate, 372.5mg sodium, 356.2mg potassium.

Multigrain English Muffins

1/2 cup warm water (105°–115°)
1 Tbs honey
2 tsp active dry yeast
1 tsp canola oil
2 1/2 cups whole wheat flour
1/4 cup rolled oats
1/4 cup wheat germ
1 Tbs coarse salt
2 tsp flaxseed meal (finely ground flaxseed)
1 tsp caraway seeds (optional)
1/2 cup plain soy yogurt
2 Tbs plain soy milk
1/8 cup cornmeal

1   Combine warm water, honey, yeast, and oil in a bowl. Let stand until foamy, about 5 minutes.

2   Using a mixer with a dough hook attachment or by hand, combine flour, oats, wheat germ, salt, flax, and caraway seeds (if desired).

3   With mixer on low speed, or by hand, knead in the yeast mixture and the yogurt and milk. Knead until smooth, about 3 or 4 minutes.

4   Lightly coat a large mixing bowl with canola oil, and place dough in bowl. Cover with plastic and let rise in a warm, dry place until doubled in size, about 1 hour.

5   Turn out dough onto a lightly floured surface, knead dough for about 1 minute, and roll to 1/2-inch thickness. Using a 3-inch round cutter, cut out rounds. Gather scraps and roll

out once more. Dust rounds with cornmeal and gently cover with plastic. Let rise until puffy, about 20 minutes.

6   Heat a large griddle or 12-inch skillet over low heat. Working in batches, place rounds 1 1/2 inches apart. Cook until golden brown and dry, about 7 minutes per side. Let cool for 30 minutes.

7   Muffins can be stored, wrapped in plastic, for 2 days, or refrigerated (up to 1 week) or frozen (up to 2 months).

Servings: 15

Nutrition (per serving): 105 calories, 1.4g total fat, 19.8g carbohydrates, 3.4g fiber, 1.2g sugar, 4.8g protein, 11.4IU vitamin a, <1mg vitamin c, 29.3mg calcium, 1.3mg iron, <1mg vitamin b6, 55.4mcg folate, 474.1mg sodium, 166mg potassium.

No-Knead, No-Work, No-Fail Whole Wheat Bread

This bread tastes best when freshly ground whole wheat flour is used.

> 7 1/2 cups whole wheat flour
> 2 pkgs (2 Tbs) dry yeast
> 4 cups warm water
> 3 1/2 Tbs honey
> 2 tsp salt

1   In a mixing bowl, put 1 cup warm water (about 100°–110° F), 1 tablespoon honey, and the yeast together and let stand for 5 minutes. If this mixture rises and gets foamy, then the yeast is good. If it doesn't rise, start over with fresh yeast. (This is easy to do in a measuring glass where you can see if the mixture rises.)

2   Mix the flour, salt, remaining honey, remaining warm water, and yeast mixture. Mix well.

3   Grease 2 loaf pans and spoon batter into them. Let rise in a warm dry place for about 15–20 minutes.

4   Preheat the oven to 375° F. Bake for 30–40 minutes. Remove and cool before slicing.

Servings: 24

Nutrition (per serving): 154 calories, <1g total fat, 32.7g carbohydrates, 1.3g fiber, 2.6g sugar, 4.4g protein, <1IU vitamin a, <1mg vitamin c, 7.6mg calcium, 2mg iron, <1mg vitamin b6, 95mcg folate, 196mg sodium, 63.4mg potassium.

Nutty Granola

cooking spray
3 cups old-fashioned oats
1/2 cup chopped, raw, unsalted walnuts
1/2 cup chopped unsalted almonds
1/2 cup chopped unsalted pecans
1/2 cup maple syrup
1/4 tsp salt
1/4 tsp ground cinnamon
1/2 cup raisins

This simple granola is great over yogurt and berries, or simply pour a hearty bowl with soymilk.

1 Preheat the oven to 300° F. Spray a large baking sheet with cooking spray.

2 In a medium bowl, combine the oats, nuts, maple syrup, salt, cinnamon, and raisins. Spread the mixture onto the baking sheet and bake until golden brown, stirring occasionally, about 30 minutes. Transfer the sheet to a cooling rack and let cool completely. Store in the refrigerator in an airtight container.

Servings: 9

Nutrition (per serving): 311 calories, 14.8g total fat, 40.6g carbohydrates, 5g fiber, 17.3g sugar, 7.9g protein, 10.4IU vitamin a, <1mg vitamin c, 62.7mg calcium, 2.3mg iron, <1mg vit. b6, 19mcg folate, 68.6mg sodium, 312.6mg potassium.

Simple Old-Fashioned Granola

4 cups regular rolled oats
2 cups shredded coconut, unsweetened
1 cup sliced almonds
1/4 cup honey
1/2 cup canola oil

1   Mix above ingredients well and spread on a baking sheet. Bake at 350° F for about 20 minutes or until golden brown. Watch so it doesn't burn, and stir once or twice.

Servings: 14

Nutrition (per serving): 288 calories, 19.7g total fat, 24.3g carbohydrates, 4.8g fiber, 6.4g sugar, 6.5g protein, <1IU vitamin a, <1mg vitamin c, 40.7mg calcium, 1.7mg iron, <1mg vitamin b6, 11.5mcg folate, 4.3mg sodium, 201.7mg potassium.

Vanilla Spice Oatmeal

3 1/2 cups water
1/4 tsp salt
2 cups old-fashioned oats
1/2 cup raisins
1/2 cup walnuts, coarsely chopped (optional)
1/4 tsp vanilla extract
pinch nutmeg
2 Tbs honey
1 cup lowfat soy milk
1/8 tsp ground cinnamon

1 In a medium saucepan, bring the water and salt to a boil. Stir in the oats and raisins, reduce the heat to low and simmer uncovered, stirring occasionally, for 5 minutes.

2 In the meantime, place nuts, if using, in a dry skillet over a medium-high flame, and toast, stirring frequently, until golden and fragrant, about 5 minutes. Set aside.

3 When the oats are cooked, remove pan from the flame and stir in the vanilla and nutmeg. Swirl in the brown sugar and place the oatmeal in serving bowls. Pour 1/4 cup of milk on top of each bowl, and top with toasted nuts and a sprinkle of cinnamon.

Note: For a quicker version using quick cooking or plain instant oatmeal, cook the oatmeal according to the directions on the package. Stir raisins, honey, and nutmeg into the cooked oatmeal. Top with milk, nuts (toasted or untoasted), and cinnamon.

Servings: 4

Nutrition (per serving): 257 calories, 2.9g total fat, 52.8g carbohydrates, 4.8g fiber, 21.5g sugar, 7.6g protein, 31.5IU vitamin a, <1mg vitamin c, 60.3mg calcium, 2.3mg iron, <1mg vit. b6, 15.8mcg folate, 159.8mg sodium, 316.8mg potassium.

Granola with Cashews,
Dried Fruit, and Wheat Germ, p. 83

Main Courses

Baked Leek and Sweet Potato Gratin

1 1/2 Tbs extra virgin olive oil, divided
3 medium leeks, white and light green
   parts chopped (6 cups)
3 cloves garlic, minced
3 Tbs chopped fresh rosemary, divided
2 medium sweet potatoes (2 pounds),
   peeled and cut into 1/8-inch thick slices
1/3 cup low-sodium vegetable broth
3 Tbs seasoned dry bread crumbs

1 Preheat oven to 450° F. Coat 10-inch round pan with cooking spray.

2 Heat 1 tablespoon oil in nonstick skillet over medium-high heat. Add leeks, garlic, and 1 1/2 tablespoons rosemary; sauté 8 minutes, or until softened. Season with salt and pepper.

3 Arrange one-third of the sweet potato slices over bottom of prepared pan, overlapping slightly. Spread half of the leek mixture on top. Arrange another one-third sweet potato slices over leeks. Top with remaining leeks, followed by remaining sweet potatoes. Drizzle broth over dish. Cover pan with foil and bake 35 mintues.

4 Stir together breadcrumbs, remaining oil, and rosemary in a small bowl. Remove foil from gratin and sprinkle with breadcrumb mixture. Bake, uncovered, 15 minutes, or until breadcrumbs are browned and crisp. Let gratin slightly cool before cutting into 8 wedges.

Servings: 8

Nutrition (per serving): 152 calories, 2.2g total fat, 31g carbohydrates, 4.4g fiber, 6.2g sugar, 3g protein, 16837.9IU vitamin a, 7.4mg vitamin c, 63.9mg calcium, 1.7mg iron, <1mg vit. b6, 38.1mcg folate, 155.7mg sodium, 472.1mg potassium.

Chickpea and Green Bean Tagine

1 1/2 cups mixed dried fruit
1 Tbs extra virgin olive oil
1 large yellow onion, chopped
2 cloves garlic, minced
1/2 tsp ground cinnamon
1/4 tsp turmeric
1/8 tsp ground allspice
8 oz green beans, cut into 1-inch pieces
1 can (15 oz) diced tomatoes in juice
1 1/2 cups vegetable stock
1 tsp honey
salt and freshly ground black pepper, to taste
1 can (15 oz) chickpeas, drained and
    rinsed (or 1 1/2 cups cooked)
1/4 cup slivered almonds
2 Tbs fresh parsley, minced
1 tsp lemon zest

1 Place the dried fruit in a small heatproof bowl. Add boiling water to cover and soak for 20 minutes to soften. Drain, coarsely chop, and set aside.

2 Heat olive oil in a large saucepan, or tagine, over medium heat. Add the onion, cover, and cook until softened, about 5 minutes. Stir in garlic, cinnamon, turmeric, and allspice. Cook, stirring, for 30 seconds. Add the green beans, tomatoes and juice, stock, honey, and salt and pepper to taste. Reduce heat to low and simmer until green beans are tender.

3 Add the reserved fruit and the chickpeas, and cook for 5 to 10 minutes to blend the flavors. Stir in the almonds, parsley,

and lemon zest. Taste and adjust seasonings, then serve hot. Serve over couscous, quinoa, or rice.

Servings: 4

Nutrition (per serving): 424 calories, 9.5g total fat, 83.3g carbohydrates, 14.6g fiber, 9.2g sugar, 10.1g protein, 2523.5IU vitamin a, 40.4mg vit. c, 150.1mg calcium, 5mg iron, <1mg vit. b6, 102.3mcg folate, 537.3mg sodium, 1286.5mg potassium.

Couscous and Vegetables

1 1/2 cups water
4 green onions, chopped
1 can (15 oz) kidney beans, rinsed and drained
1 cup whole wheat couscous
3 Tbs extra virgin olive oil
1 small onion, chopped
1 clove garlic, minced
3 medium tomatoes, chopped
1/2 pound baby spinach leaves, chopped
1 medium bell pepper, seeded and chopped
1 small zucchini, chopped
1/4 pound carrots, chopped
1 tsp paprika
1 tsp salt
1/2 tsp cumin
1/2 tsp pepper

1   Bring the green onions and water to a boil. Turn off heat and add whole wheat couscous and kidney beans. Cover and let stand 10 minutes.

2   Meanwhile, sauté onions and garlic in olive oil for 3 minutes or until tender and golden. Add the remaining ingredients and cook another 10 minutes.

3   Uncover couscous and fluff gently with a fork. Gently stir vegetable mixture into the couscous and serve.

Servings: 6

Nutrition (per serving): 250 calories, 7.5g total fat, 38.4g carbohydrates, 7.5g fiber, 4.2g sugar, 9.1g protein, 6736.6IU vitamin a, 42.4mg vitamin c, 90.1mg calcium, 3mg iron, <1mg vit. b6, 130.9mcg folate, 514.1mg sodium, 724mg potassium.

Fajitas

12 whole wheat tortillas
1 can (15 oz) pinto beans, rinsed and drained
1 Tbs extra virgin olive oil
1 white onion, sliced
1 red bell pepper, seeded and thinly sliced lengthwise
1 tsp cumin
1/2 tsp garlic powder
pinch chili powder
salt and freshly ground black pepper, to taste
2 tomatoes
1 can (11 oz) corn
1 cup romaine lettuce, shredded
1 1/2 cups guacamole

1   Heat olive oil in a large skillet over medium heat. Add sliced
    onion and pepper. Cook until softened, about 10–15 min-
    utes. Add salt, pepper, cumin, garlic powder and chili pow-
    der. Cook for 30 seconds. Increase heat to medium-high,
    add chopped tomatoes and cook for 2–3 minutes. Remove
    from heat.

2   Heat tortillas in a dry pan over low heat until warm and
    pliable.

3   To assemble fajitas, place 1 tortilla flat, add a scoop of pinto
    beans down the middle then top with a scoop of the pepper,
    onion, and tomato mixture. Add a strips of corn, guacamole,
    and lettuce on top. Roll up the edges of the tortilla like a bur-
    rito. Repeat with remaining tortillas.

Servings: 6

Nutrition (per serving): 399 calories, 15.4g total fat, 57.3g carbohydrates, 10.2g
fiber, 5.8g sugar, 11.1g protein, 1836.6IU vit. a, 62.8mg vit. c, 134.1mg calcium,
4.1mg iron, <1mg vit. b6, 182.3mcg folate, 790mg sodium, 778.8mg potassium.

Falafels

1 cup parsley, chopped
1/2 cup cilantro, chopped
1/2 jalapeno pepper
8 oz dried garbanzo beans
6 oz dried fava beans
2 cloves garlic, chopped
1 onion, chopped
1 Tbs salt
1 1/2 tsp black pepper
1 1/2 tsp allspice
1 Tbs cumin
1 Tbs coriander
1 1/2 Tbs baking powder
1/2 cup peanut or canola oil, for cooking

1   Soak the garbanzo beans and the fava beans immersed together in cold water for 24 hours. Drain beans. In the food processor, process the parsley, cilantro, jalapeno (seeded for less heat), garlic, beans, and onions. Mix well with the spices and baking powder.

2   To cook, heat up the oil in a large pan over medium high heat. Form the falafel mixture into balls about 2–3 Tbs each. (I like to use a small ice cream scoop.) In a large sauté pan over medium heat, pan fry the balls until all sides are brown and crisp, about 10 minutes.

3   Serve in whole wheat pita with lettuce, tomato, thinly sliced red onion, and tahini or hummus. Great sprinkled with sesame seeds.

Servings: 12

Nutrition (per serving): 83 calories, <1g total fat, 15g carbohydrates, 5.1g fiber, 1.3g sugar, 5.1g protein, 564IU vitamin a, 9.6mg vitamin c, 43.6mg calcium, 2.1mg iron, <1mg vitamin b6, 83.8mcg folate, 646.7mg sodium, 258.6mg potassium.

Grilled Skewers with Rosemary-Dijon Vinaigrette

Rosemary-Dijon Vinaigrette
4 Tbs sherry vinegar
4 Tbs Dijon mustard
2 small shallots, minced
2 Tbs lemon juice
1 Tbs lemon zest
2/3 cup extra virgin olive oil
2 Tbs chopped fresh rosemary

Vegetable Skewers
6 small red potatoes, quartered
24 sugar snap peas
24 white or cremini mushrooms, stems removed
1 red bell pepper, cut into 1-inch pieces
1 red onion, cut into 1-inch pieces
1 medium yellow squash, cut into 12 rounds
1 medium zucchini, cut into 12 rounds

1. To make the Rosemary-Dijon Vinaigrette: Whisk together vinegar, mustard, shallots, lemon juice, and lemon zest in a small bowl. Slowly whisk in olive oil until mixture thickens. Stir in rosemary, and season with salt and pepper. Set aside.

2. To make Vegetable Skewers: Cook potatoes 3 minutes in a large pot of salted boiling water. Add snap peas, and cook 1 minute more. Drain vegetables, and rinse under cold water. Pat dry.

3   Toss potatoes, snap peas, mushrooms, red bell pepper, red onion, yellow squash, and zucchini with 1/2 cup Rosemary-Dijon Vinaigrette. Cover and refrigerate 1 hour, or overnight.

4   Preheat grill to medium-high heat. Thread vegetables onto 12 presoaked bamboo skewers, leaving 1/4-inch space between vegetables to ensure even cooking.

5   Rub grill with vegetable oil. Grill skewers 3 to 4 minutes per side, or until vegetables are slightly charred and soft. Season with salt and pepper. Serve with remaining 1/4 cup vinaigrette on the side for dipping.

Servings: 6

Nutrition (per serving): 165 calories, 8g total fat, 21.1g carbohydrates, 4g fiber, 4g sugar, 5.5g protein, 1068.7IU vitamin a, 74.8mg vitamin c, 32.1mg calcium, 1.6mg iron, <1mg vitamin b6, 48.7mcg folate, 84.4mg sodium, 826mg potassium.

Falafels, p. 103

Pizza

1 1/4 cups warm water (105°–115°)
2 Tbs dry yeast
1 Tbs honey
3 Tbs plus 2 tsp extra virgin olive oil
3–4 cups whole wheat flour
2 tsp kosher salt
3/4 cup store-bought marinara or pizza sauce
6 button mushrooms, chopped
1 bell pepper, sliced
1/2 onion, sliced
1/4 cup sliced black olives
1/2 pint cherry tomatoes, halved
1 tsp dried oregano
fresh basil leaves

1   For the dough: Mix together warm water, yeast, honey, and olive oil. Let sit for about 5 minutes. Make sure that the yeast is foamy.

2   Using a mixer with a dough hook, or by hand, slowly add in 3 cups of flour and 2 tsp salt. Knead the dough on low speed, or by hand, for 10 minutes. Add flour as needed if the dough is sticky.

3   Place dough onto a lightly floured surface and knead by hand 12 times. Put dough in a well-oiled bowl, and roll dough around so that all sides are lightly coated in olive oil. Cover with a clean cloth. Let rise until double in volume, about 30–50 minutes.

4   Divide the dough into equal parts (makes 2–6 pizzas, depending on how big you want them). Roll dough into balls and cover with a damp towel to rest 10 minutes.

5   On a lightly floured surface, roll out dough to about 1/4-inch thick. Sprinkle a light layer of cornmeal on baking sheet or pizza stone.

6   Spread out pizza sauce evenly over pizzas, leaving a 1/2-inch border around the outside of the dough. Evenly top pizza with toppings. Sprinkle on dried oregano and drizzle over olive oil over the top.

7   Bake 10–15 minutes at 400° F (or 500° F if you like the crust extra crispy). Remove from oven and top with basil leaves. Let cool 10 minutes before slicing and serving.

Servings: 8

Nutrition (per serving): 348 calories, 11.1g total fat, 55.9g carbohydrates, 9.6g fiber, 7.3g sugar, 11.5g protein, 465IU vitamin a, 28.8mg vit. c, 48.1mg calcium, 3.9mg iron, <1mg vit. b6, 135.6mcg folate, 836.2mg sodium, 619.6mg potassium.

Spring Vegetable Tagine

1 Tbs extra virgin olive oil
8 oz cipollini onions, peeled and trimmed
12 oz fingerling potatoes
1/4 tsp cinnamon
1/2 tsp coriander
1/2 tsp cumin
3/4 cup vegetable stock
8 oz baby carrots, peeled and trimmed
8 oz zucchini, cut into 1/2-inch slices
8 oz summer squash, cut into 1/2-inch slices
8 oz haricots verts, ends trimmed
salt and freshly ground black pepper, to taste
finely grated lemon zest of 1 lemon
2 Tbs chopped fresh parsley
steamed wheat couscous or brown rice, for serving

1   In a tagine over medium heat, warm the olive oil. Add the onions and cook until lightly browned on both sides, about 4 minutes.

2   Add the potatoes, spices and 1/2 cup of the stock. Cover the tagine with the lid and cook for 15 minutes. Add the carrots, cover, and cook for 12 minutes.

3   Add the squash, zucchini and the remaining 1/4 cup stock, and season with salt and pepper. Cover and cook for 5 minutes. Add the haricots verts, cover, and cook for 5 minutes. Stir in the lemon zest and parsley. Serve the tagine warm with steamed couscous or cooked rice.

Servings: 6

Nutrition (per serving): 219 calories, 3.5g total fat, 42.9g carbohydrates, 6.5g fiber, 4.5g sugar, 5.9g protein, 5735.5IU vitamin a, 38mg vitamin c, 69.1mg calcium, 2.2mg iron, <1mg vit. b6, 67mcg folate, 141.8mg sodium, 703.5mg potassium.

Vegetable Chow Mein

1/2 pound fresh Chinese noodles,
   or whole wheat angel hair
5 Tbs corn or peanut oil
2 Tbs soy sauce
2 Tbs rice vinegar
2 Tbs Asian sesame oil
1/2 yellow onion, thinly sliced
1 red bell pepper, seeded and thinly sliced lengthwise
1/4 pound shiitake mushrooms, caps thinly sliced
1 cup snow peas, thinly sliced (optional)
1 zucchini, trimmed and cut into matchsticks
1 Tbs fresh grated ginger
2 cloves garlic, minced

1 Parboil the noodles and make the sauce. Bring a large pot of water to a boil over high heat. Add the noodles and boil for 2 minutes. Drain the noodles in a colander and rinse well with cold running water. Place in a bowl, add 1 Tbs of the corn oil, and toss to coat evenly.

2 In a small bowl, combine 3 Tbs water, soy sauce, vinegar, and sesame oil and stir.

3 Stir-fry the vegetables. Heat a wok or large fry pan over high heat until very hot and add 2 Tbs of the corn oil. Add the onion and bell pepper and stir-fry just until tender, about 2 minutes. Add the mushrooms, peas, and zucchini and continue to stir-fry until golden brown, about 2 minutes. Using a slotted spoon, transfer the vegetables to a bowl.

4 Stir-fry the noodles. Return the pan to high heat and add the remaining 2 Tbs corn oil. Add the ginger and garlic and stir-fry until fragrant, about 5 seconds. Add the noodles and cook until heated through, about 5 minutes. Return the vegetables to the pan, add the sauce, and continue to stir and toss until all the ingredients are well combined and heated through, about 1 minute. Transfer to a platter and serve immediately.

Servings: 4

Nutrition (per serving): 344 calories, 11.5g total fat, 58g carbohydrates, 2.3g fiber, 4.4g sugar, 10.6g protein, 1239.4IU vitamin a, 79.3mg vitamin c, 47.9mg calcium, 3.1mg iron, <1mg vit. b6, 65.8mcg folate, 559mg sodium, 476.3mg potassium.

Pasta and Pasta Salads

Beets and Bowtie

1/3 cup pine nuts
4 Tbs extra virgin olive oil, divided
2 large onions, quartered then sliced
3 cloves garlic, minced
2 bunches golden beets, peeled and cut into 8 wedges each,
    and greens cut into 1-inch strips
12 oz whole wheat farfalle (bowtie pasta)

1 Heat heavy large skillet over medium heat. Add pine nuts and stir until lightly toasted, about 3 minutes. Set aside.

2 In the same skillet, sauté onion with 2 tablespoons oil until the onions begin to soften, about 10 minutes. Reduce heat to medium-low and continue to sauté until onions are tender and browned, about 30 minutes longer. Add garlic and stir 2 minutes. Scatter beet greens over onions. Drizzle remaining 2 tablespoons oil over the top; cover and cook until beet greens are tender, about 5 minutes.

3 Meanwhile, cook beets in a large pot of boiling salted water until tender, about 10 minutes. Remove with slotted spoon. Return water to a boil and add the pasta, cooking until al dente. Drain, reserving 1 cup cooking water. Return pasta to pot.

4 Stir onion-green mixture and beets into pasta. Add pasta cooking liquid by 1/4 cupfuls to moisten. Season with salt and pepper. Divide pasta among shallow bowls. Sprinkle with pine nuts.

Servings: 4

Nutrition (per serving): 538 calories, 22.5g total fat, 76.4g carbohydrates, 2g fiber, 5.6g sugar, 15.3g protein, 13.5IU vitamin a, 6.5mg vitamin c, 60.7mg calcium, 4.2mg iron, <1mg vit. b6, 86.9mcg folate, 29.4mg sodium, 444.4mg potassium.

Bowties with Fresh Tomato Sauce

4 tomatoes peeled, seeded and diced (about 2 pounds)
1/2 cup fresh basil leaves, julienned,
  plus whole leaves for garnish
3 Tbs chopped red onion
3 Tbs extra virgin olive oil
1 Tbs red wine vinegar
1 clove garlic, minced
3/4 tsp salt
1/4 tsp freshly ground black pepper
1/2 pound whole wheat bowtie or farfalle pasta

1. In a large bowl, combine the tomatoes, julienned basil, onion, olive oil, vinegar, garlic, salt and pepper. Toss gently to mix.

2. Bring a large pot of salted water to a boil. Add the pasta and cook until al dente, about 10 minutes. Drain the pasta well. Divide pasta among individual bowls and top with sauce. Garnish with a fresh basil leaf.

Servings: 4

Nutrition (per serving): 318 calories, 11.3g total fat, 49.4g carbohydrates, 2g fiber, 3.6g sugar, 9.8g protein, 1405.6IU vitamin a, 18.4mg vitamin c, 48.4mg calcium, 2.8mg iron, <1mg vit. b6, 56.2mcg folate, 448.3mg sodium, 475.9mg potassium.

Garden Pasta Salad

1 pound whole wheat spiral pasta
1 large carrot, diced
2 stalks celery, diced
1 cup bell peppers, diced (assortment of colors)
1 pint grape tomatoes, halved
3/4 cup frozen corn, thawed or fresh
1/2 cup chopped green onion
8 oz Italian-style salad dressing

1 Cook pasta in large pot of boiling water until al dente, then drain.

2 Mix carrots, celery, peppers, tomatoes, and green onion together in large bowl. Add the cooled pasta and mix together. Pour desired amount of dressing over mixture and mix well. Chill before serving.

Servings: 10

Nutrition (per serving): 251 calories, 7.4g total fat, 42.5g carbohydrates, 1.4g fiber, 3.6g sugar, 7.7g protein, 1635IU vitamin a, 36.9mg vitamin c, 32.6mg calcium, 2.2mg iron, <1mg vit. b6, 47.2mcg folate, 421.1mg sodium, 293.6mg potassium.

Garlic Spaghetti Primavera

1 slice day-old whole grain crusty bread
2 1/2 Tbs extra virgin olive oil
4 cloves garlic, thinly sliced
1 1/2 Tbs finely chopped walnuts
1/4 cup chopped fresh flat-leaf parsley
1 tsp salt
1 small yellow squash, cut into 2-inch strips
1 small zucchini, cut into 2-inch strips
1 cup shredded carrot
1 small red bell pepper, cut into 2-inch strips
1/4 cup diced yellow bell pepper
1/2 tsp freshly ground black pepper
1/2 pound whole wheat spaghetti

1   In a blender or food processor, process the bread to make fine crumbs. In a large nonstick frying pan, heat 1 1/2 tsp olive oil over medium heat. Add the sliced garlic and sauté until lightly golden brown, about 1 minute. Stir in bread crumbs and cook another 3–4 minutes. Transfer to a bowl and stir in walnuts, parsley, and 1/2 tsp salt; set aside.

2   Bring a large pot of salted water to a boil. Add the spaghetti and cook until al dente, about 10 minutes. Drain well.

3   Meanwhile, add the remaining 2 Tbs oil to the pan over medium heat. Add the yellow squash, zucchini, and carrot and sauté until crisp-tender, about 5 minutes. Transfer to a plate.

4   Add the bell peppers to the pan and saute until they begin to soften, about 2 minutes. Stir in 1/2 tsp salt and 1/2 tsp pepper. Return the squash mixture to the pan.

5   In a shallow serving bowl, combine the spaghetti, vegetables, and bread crumb mixture. Toss gently to mix and serve.

Servings: 4

Nutrition (per serving): 342 calories, 11.7g total fat, 53.7g carbohydrates, 2.7g fiber, 4.3g sugar, 11g protein, 3686.8IU vitamin a, 74.7mg vitamin c, 61.5mg calcium, 3.2mg iron, <1mg vit. b6, 72.3mcg folate, 647.6mg sodium, 478.6mg potassium.

Hearty Pasta with Sautéed Vegetables

1/2 pound whole wheat rigatoni
1 clove garlic, minced
1 shallot, finely chopped
3 Tbs extra virgin olive oil
1 zucchini, diced
2 cups baby spinach leaves
3 roma tomatoes, chopped
1/3 cup fresh basil, chopped
1/4 cup walnuts, chopped
salt and freshly ground black pepper, to taste

1   Bring a large pot of salted water to a boil and add the whole wheat rigatoni. Cook until al dente. Reserve 1/2 cup of the pasta water.

2   Meanwhile, in a large sauté pan, heat olive oil over medium high heat and sauté shallot and garlic 3–4 minutes. Then add the zucchini and cook another couple of minutes until lightly tender. Add the spinach leaves and cook until wilted. Add salt and pepper to taste. Add the tomatoes to the pan and cook 1 minute before adding the pasta and the walnuts. Add pasta water if necessary to keep the sauce moist and loose. Remove from heat and mix in basil.

Servings: 6

Nutrition (per serving): 417 calories, 11.2g total fat, 71.4g carbohydrates, 1.3g fiber, 1.4g sugar, 14.5g protein, 2104.7IU vitamin a, 17.4mg vit. c, 81.5mg calcium, 4.3mg iron, <1mg vit. b6, 104.8mcg folate, 26.9mg sodium, 617.6mg potassium.

Pasta Puttanesca

8 oz whole wheat spaghetti
1 Tbs extra virgin olive oil
2 cloves garlic, minced
1/3 cup flat-leaf parsley, chopped
1/4 cup pitted chopped Spanish or Greek olives
2 Tbs capers
1 Tbs fresh oregano leaves (or 1 tsp dried)
1/8 tsp crushed red pepper flakes
1 can (14 oz) diced tomatoes
3/4 cup chopped fresh arugula
1/4 cup vegan parmesan cheese

1 Bring a large pot of water to a boil. Add pasta and cook according to the directions on the package.

2 While the pasta is cooking, heat the oil in a large skillet over medium heat. Add the garlic and sauté until fragrant, about 1 minute. Add the parsley, olives, capers, oregano and crushed red pepper to the skillet, and sauté for 2 minutes more. Add the canned tomatoes and simmer for about 5 minutes. Stir in the arugula and simmer for 1 minute more, until the greens wilt slightly.

3 When the pasta is done, drain and add it to the skillet, tossing with the sauce to combine. Top with grated cheese, if desired.

Servings: 4

Nutrition (per serving): 305 calories, 8.5g total fat, 52.3g carbohydrates, 2.6g fiber, <1g sugar, 10.6g protein, 1294.6IU vitamin a, 18mg vitamin c, 92.7mg calcium, 4.3mg iron, <1mg vit. b6, 57.7mcg folate, 358.1mg sodium, 470.3mg potassium.

Savory Pasta Crumbles

This makes a Parmesan-like topping for pasta dishes.

1/2 cup buckwheat groats
2 Tbs extra virgin olive oil
3 cloves garlic, minced
1/4 cup plus 1 Tbs nutritional yeast, divided
2 tsp salt

1 Place buckwheat groats in medium bowl and cover with 3 inches cold water. Soak 12 hours. Drain.

2 Preheat oven to 300° F. Line baking sheet with parchment paper. Heat oil and garlic in saucepan over low heat until hot. Toss buckwheat groats with garlic oil in bowl. Stir in 1/4 cup nutritional yeast and salt.

3 Spread buckwheat groats in even layer on prepared baking sheet. Sprinkle with remaining 1 Tbs yeast. Bake 30 minutes, or until completely dry and crunchy. Cool, and store in airtight container.

Servings: 8

Nutrition (per serving): 85 calories, 3.9g total fat, 10.4g carbohydrates, 2.3g fiber, <1g sugar, 3.6g protein, 0IU vitamin a, <1mg vitamin c, 8mg calcium, 1.3mg iron, <1mg vitamin b6, 144.7mcg folate, 585.8mg sodium, 157.5mg potassium.

Simple Shells

1/2 pound whole wheat pasta shells
1/4 cup extra virgin olive oil
2 large fresh tomatoes, chopped
1/2 cup fresh basil, chopped
salt and freshly ground black pepper, to taste

1 Add the pasta to a large pot of salted boiling water and cook until al dente.

2 Drain pasta and immediately mix in oil, tomatoes, and basil. Season with salt and pepper. Serve warm or at room temperature.

Servings: 4

Nutrition (per serving): 137 calories, 13.7g total fat, 3.8g carbohydrates, 1.3g fiber, 2.4g sugar, <1g protein, 1037.6IU vitamin a, 12.5mg vitamin c, 17.4mg calcium, <1mg iron, <1mg vitamin b6, 17mcg folate, 5.2mg sodium, 240.3mg potassium.

Spaghetti with Mushrooms

1 pound whole wheat spaghetti
2 Tbs extra virgin olive oil
3 cloves garlic, minced
1 onion, chopped
3 green onions, chopped
1/2 portobello mushroom, sliced
1 cup oyster mushrooms, sliced
3/4 cup crimini mushrooms, sliced
1/4 cup fresh parsley, chopped
1/4 cup fresh basil, chopped
3 Tbs fresh rosemary leaves, chopped
1 Tbs dried oregano
2 Tbs garlic salt
1 Tbs black pepper
1/2 Tbs onion powder
1 Tbs Italian seasoning
1 cube mushroom bullion
2 cans (15 oz each) Italian tomatoes
1 can (28 oz) whole tomatoes, drained
1 can (6 oz) tomato paste
2 1/2 cups water
1 cup fresh tomatoes, chopped
1 tsp red pepper flakes
extra chopped fresh parsley and basil for serving

1 Heat oil in a large skillet over medium heat. Sauté garlic, onion, mushrooms, and rosemary until onions are tender and slightly translucent, about 6 minutes. Add parsley, basil, oregano, garlic salt, pepper, onion powder, Italian seasoning, and mushroom bullion. Stir for 1 minute. Add tomatoes,

tomato paste and water, and boil 5 minutes. Add fresh tomatoes and red pepper flakes.

2 Reduce heat to low and simmer for 60–90 minutes, stirring often. Taste and add salt if necessary.

3 Cook spaghetti noodles in a large pot of boiling salted water until al dente, about 8 minutes. Add cooked noodles to sauce. Sprinkle top with fresh herbs and serve.

Servings: 6

Nutrition (per serving): 413 calories, 6.5g total fat, 80.7g carbohydrates, 7.1g fiber, 10.2g sugar, 17.4g protein, 1363.8IU vit. a, 34.2mg vit. c, 141.7mg calcium, 7.2mg iron, <1mg vit. b6, 109.3mcg folate, 2477.6mg sodium, 1309.2mg potassium.

Veggie Fest Pasta

1 pound whole wheat short cut pasta, penne or rotini
2 Tbs extra virgin olive oil
4 green onions, white and light green parts, chopped
2 cloves garlic, minced
2 carrots, chopped
5 button mushrooms, sliced
1 bag (7 oz) baby spinach leaves
1/4 cup white wine or 1/4 cup vegetable stock
1 pint cherry or grape tomatoes, halved
1 can (15 oz) cannellini beans, rinsed and drained
1/4 tsp Italian seasoning

1   Cook pasta in salted water until al dente. Drain and set aside.

2   Heat oil in a large saucepan over medium heat. Add green onions and garlic; sauté 2 minutes. Add carrots and mushrooms, and cook 3 minutes more. Stir in spinach and wine, and cook 2 to 3 minutes, or until spinach wilts.

3   Stir in tomatoes, beans, and Italian seasoning, and cook 3 to 4 minutes, or until heated through. Fold in pasta. Serve.

Servings: 6

Nutrition (per serving): 442 calories, 3.8g total fat, 82.8g carbohydrates, 10.7g fiber, 2.3g sugar, 23.4g protein, 6604.9IU vit. a, 15.5mg vit. c, 209.7mg calcium, 9.2mg iron, <1mg vit. b6, 110.2mcg folate, 61.5mg sodium, 1522.4mg potassium.

Whole Wheat Spaghetti with Sautéed Leeks, White Beans, and Walnuts

1 Tbs extra virgin olive oil
3 medium leeks, white and light green parts, chopped
1 medium yellow bell pepper, seeded and thinly sliced
1/4 tsp red pepper flakes
1 can (15 oz) cannellini beans, rinsed and drained
1 cup vegetable broth
3 cloves garlic, minced
12 oz whole wheat spaghetti
1/3 cup chopped toasted walnuts

1   Heat oil in a large saucepan over medium-high heat. Add leeks, bell pepper, and red pepper flakes; sauté 10 minutes, or until vegetables begin to brown. Stir in beans, vegetable broth, and garlic. Reduce heat to low, and simmer 5 minutes. Season with salt and pepper, if desired.

2   Meanwhile, cook spaghetti until al dente, about 7 minutes. Drain and divide pasta among 4 bowls. Spoon sauce over each serving of pasta and sprinkle with walnuts.

Servings: 4

Nutrition (per serving): 606 calories, 10.5g total fat, 109.1g carbohydrates, 10g fiber, 2.9g sugar, 27.4g protein, 1207.7IU vit. a, 94.2mg vit. c, 213.5mg calcium, 10.3mg iron, <1mg vit. b6, 113.2mcg folate, 29.8mg sodium, 1361mg potassium.

Whole Wheat Pasta with Broccoli Rabe

1 large bunch broccoli rabe
Kosher salt
1 pound farro linguine or whole wheat linguine
2 Tbs extra virgin olive oil
1 cup chopped red onions
2 cups low sodium vegetable broth or pasta water
3 roasted garlic cloves or 3 tsp jarred roasted garlic
freshly ground black pepper

1 Trim off the tough stem ends from the braccoli rabe and discard. Cut the florets off, then coarsely chop the leaves and tender stems and set aside.

2 Bring a large pot of water to a boil, add 2 Tbs salt and the pasta, and cook until al dente.

3 While the water is heating, in a large fry pan over medium-high heat, warm the olive oil. Add the onions and cook until soft, about 4 minutes. Stir in half of the greens, including florets. Cook another 2–3 minutes. Add the remaining greens and cook another 5 minutes. Pour in the broth or pasta water and mix in the garlic. Reduce the heat to medium and simmer until the broccoli rabe is tender, about 10 minutes. Season with salt and pepper.

4 When pasta is done, top with greens. If the greens are dry, add some reserved pasta water. Serve at once.

Servings: 6

Nutrition (per serving): 355 calories, 6g total fat, 67.2g carbohydrates, 3.4g fiber, 1.9g sugar, 14.7g protein, 748.8IU vitamin a, 101.7mg vitamin c, 91.8mg calcium, 3.7mg iron, <1mg vit. b6, 114.8mcg folate, 91.7mg sodium, 529.5mg potassium.

Crisp Endive, Apple, and Walnut Salad, p. 132

Salads

Beet Salad with Orange Vinaigrette

4 beets
3 Tbs fresh orange juice
2 Tbs extra virgin olive oil
1 Tbs red wine vinegar
1 Tbs minced fresh dill
1 tsp grated orange zest
1/4 tsp minced garlic
kosher salt and freshly ground black pepper
3 green onions, including green tops, sliced diagonally
10 oz mixed salad greens (about 8 cups loosely packed)
1/2 cup thinly sliced English cucumbers

1   Preheat oven to 400° F. Trim off the leafy green tops from the beets. Wrap the beets individually in squares of aluminum foil, tightly securing the foil. Place on baking sheet and bake until tender when pierced, about 1 hour.

2   Let beets cool. Peel off loosened skins and cut beets crosswise into 4 or 5 slices. Place in bowl.

3   Whisk together the orange juice, olive oil, vinegar, minced dill, orange zest, garlic, and 1/2 tsp salt and pepper.

4   Pour all but 2 Tbs of the vinaigrette over the beets. Add half of the green onions and stir gently to blend. Separately, toss the salad greens and reserved dressing.

5   Arrange the salad greens on a platter or individual plates. Place beets on top of greens. Tuck the cucumbers in among the beets. Drizzle with any remaining dressing from the bowl, and sprinkle with the rest of the onions.

Servings: 4

Nutrition (per serving): 125 calories, 7g total fat, 15.6g carbohydrates, 2.6g fiber, 6g sugar, 2g protein, 443.2IU vitamin a, 34.3mg vitamin c, 33.7mg calcium, 1.2mg iron, <1mg vitamin b6, 91.3mcg folate, 317.3mg sodium, 333.5mg potassium.

Best-of-Summer Fruit Salad

Tossing fruit in a lemon-infused syrup lightly sweetens it and keeps it from browning once it's cut and stirred into a salad. Feel free to substitute whatever fruit you may have on hand for the choices here. If you wish to use bananas, however, do not add them until just before you're ready to serve the dish.

   1/4 cup agave nectar or honey
   1/4 cup fresh mint or lemon verbena leaves
   2 Tbs lemon juice
   2 peaches or nectarines, cut into 1 1/2-inch pieces
   2 cups seedless grapes, halved
   1 cup sliced strawberries or whole raspberries
   1 cup blueberries

1 Bring agave nectar and 1/2 cup water to a boil in a saucepan. Simmer 2 minutes. Remove from heat, and stir in mint and lemon juice. Steep 15 minutes. Strain out mint.

2 Combine fruit and stir in syrup. Cover and chill 2 hours, or overnight.

Servings: 8

Nutrition (per serving): 88 calories, <1g total fat, 23g carbohydrates, 1.7g fiber, 19.8g sugar, <1g protein, 153.3IU vitamin a, 22mg vitamin c, 12.7mg calcium, <1mg iron, <1mg vitamin b6, 9.5mcg folate, 1.9mg sodium, 183.4mg potassium.

Crisp Endive, Apple, and Walnut Salad

2–3 heads Belgian endive
2 Tbs canola oil
2 Tbs fresh lemon juice
2 tsp walnut oil
1 tsp grated lemon zest
kosher salt
1/2 cup walnuts, chopped
1 small Granny Smith apple
1 small Braeburn apple
1 small Golden Delicious apple
2 Tbs chopped fresh dill

1 In a bowl, combine the Belgian endives with ice water to cover and let stand 20 minutes to crisp. Drain, pat dry and trim to bases. Set aside.

2 Whisk together the canola oil, lemon juice, walnut oil, zest, and 1/2 tsp salt until blended.

3 In a dry pan over low heat, toast the walnuts until warm and fragrant, about 5 minutes. Be careful not to burn. Remove from heat.

4 Core the apples and cut into very thin slices. Add the apples, endive, and dill to the dressing and toss. Sprinkle with walnuts. Serve at once.

Servings: 4

Nutrition (per serving): 265 calories, 19.4g total fat, 22.3g carbohydrates, 10.9g fiber, 9.5g sugar, 5.7g protein, 5627.4IU vit. a, 24.9mg vit. c, 154.3mg calcium, 2.7mg iron, <1mg vit. b6, 382.4mcg folate, 128.3mg sodium, 967.3mg potassium.

Edamame and Orange Salad

1 package (10 oz) frozen, shelled edamame
2 navel oranges
1/2 cup diced red onion
1/4 cup minced red bell pepper
3 Tbs rice vinegar
2 Tbs canola oil
1 tsp low sodium soy sauce
1/2 tsp grated orange zest
1/2 tsp grated fresh ginger
1/4 cup torn fresh cilantro

1 Cook edamame according to package directions. Drain well and set aside.

2 Cut the orange sections out of the oranges (sections should not have white membrane) and cut each section into 2 to 3 pieces.

3 In a bowl, combine the oranges, edamame, onion, and bell pepper. Whisk together the rice vinegar, oil, soy sauce, orange zest, and ginger.

4 Toss dressing and vegetables. Top with cilantro and serve.

Servings: 4

Nutrition (per serving): 212 calories, 12g total fat, 23.6g carbohydrates, 5.1g fiber, 6.2g sugar, 10.2g protein, 530.2IU vitamin a, 74.2mg vitamin c, 181.1mg calcium, 3.2mg iron, <1mg vit. b6, 143.9mcg folate, 58.5mg sodium, 666.7mg potassium.

Roasted Broccoli and Chickpea Salad, p. 139

Exotic Spinach Salad

Because the corn is raw, look for the freshest young corn you can find. If you do not like the flavor of dill, leave it out.

2 ears corn (1 cup kernels)
1 large tomato, diced and seeded
1/2 cup diced English (hothouse) cucumbers
1/2 cup diced sweet onion (Maui, Vidalia, Walla Walla)
2 Tbs chopped fresh basil
2 Tbs chopped fresh parsley
2 Tbs chopped fresh mint
2 Tbs chopped fresh dill, optional
1 tsp chopped garlic
1 tsp ground cumin
1/4 cup extra virgin olive oil
2 Tbs red wine vinegar
kosher salt and freshly ground black pepper
5 oz baby spinach leaves

1 Husk the corn ears and carefully remove all the silk. Hold one ear upright, stem end down, in the center of a wide, shallow bowl. Using a sharp knife, slice straight down between the kernels and the cob, rotating the ear a quarter turn after each cut. Repeat with the second ear. You will have about 1 cup kernels.

2 In a large salad bowl, combine the corn, tomato, cucumber, and onion. Combine the basil, mint, parsley, dill and garlic on a cutting board and finely chop. Add to the vegetables.

3   In a small, dry frying pan over medium-high heat, warm the cumin just until fragrant, about 20 seconds. Transfer to a small bowl. Add the olive oil, vinegar, 1/2 tsp salt, and a grind of pepper, and whisk until blended. Rinse the spinach and pat dry. Add the spinach and the dressing to the vegetable mixture. Toss and season with salt and pepper to taste.

Servings: 6

Nutrition (per serving): 123 calories, 9.5g total fat, 9.5g carbohydrates, 1.9g fiber, 2g sugar, 2.1g protein, 2730.1IU vitamin a, 15.4mg vitamin c, 40.4mg calcium, 1.4mg iron, <1mg vit. b6, 67.5mcg folate, 71mg sodium, 316.8mg potassium.

Farm Stand Salad

3 ears corn, husks and silk removed
1 1/2 pounds green beans, stem ends snapped off
3 cloves garlic, peeled and gently smashed
4 Tbs extra virgin olive oil
3 Tbs red wine vinegar
1/2 small red onion, peeled and thinly sliced
1 medium yellow tomato, sliced to 1/2-inch thick
2 cups mixed red and green heirloom tomatoes, halved

1   In a large pot of boiling salted water, cook the corn until tender, 5 to 7 minutes. Remove corn with tongs and set aside on a cutting board to cool. Using a strainer, remove any corn silk remaining in the pot.

2   Add the green beans, return to a boil, and cook until very tender, about 8 minutes (timing may vary depending on the size of the beans). Meanwhile, cut the corn kernels off the cobs and put kernels in a large bowl. Drain the beans in a colander, shake to remove excess water, and put in bowl with corn. Add garlic and 3 tablespoons of oil. Toss well and let stand at least 30 minutes for flavors to blend; refrigerate if longer than 30 minutes.

3   If necessary, bring beans and corn to room temperature by removing them from refrigerator 30 minutes before serving. Just before serving, remove the garlic and add the remaining tablespoon of oil along with vinegar, onion, and tomatoes. Add salt to taste and serve at room temperature.

Servings: 6

Nutrition (per serving): 172 calories, 9.7g total fat, 21.3g carbohydrates, 5.7g fiber, 3g sugar, 4.2g protein, 1180.9IU vitamin a, 37.7mg vitamin c, 54.1mg calcium, 1.9mg iron, <1mg vit. b6, 74.8mcg folate, 47.2mg sodium, 538.1mg potassium.

Frisée and Apple Salad
with Dried Cherries and Walnuts

3 Tbs extra virgin olive oil
2 Tbs apple cider vinegar
2 Tbs minced shallot
1 Tbs honey
1/2 cup dried tart cherries (3 oz)
1 large head of frisée, torn into bite-size pieces
1 medium Gala apple, cored and thinly sliced
1/2 cup coarsely chopped toasted walnuts

1   Whisk first 4 ingredients in small bowl to blend. Season dressing to taste with salt and pepper.

2   Stir in dried cherries. Toss frisée and apple slices in large bowl. Add cherry dressing and toss to coat. Divide among 4 plates; sprinkle with walnuts and freshly ground black pepper and serve.

Servings: 4

Nutrition (per serving): 290 calories, 20.1g total fat, 28.3g carbohydrates, 3.2g fiber, 8.8g sugar, 3.6g protein, 674.3IU vitamin a, 6mg vitamin c, 59.1mg calcium, 1mg iron, <1mg vitamin b6, 41.4mcg folate, 11.1mg sodium, 220.7mg potassium.

Roasted Broccoli and Chickpea Salad

2 small heads broccoli, trimmed and cut into large florets
2 Tbs extra virgin olive oil
1 large shallot, thinly sliced
1 can (11 oz) chickpeas, rinsed and drained
1 tsp sherry vinegar
1 head romaine lettuce, leaves separated
1 cup walnuts

Vinaigrette
2 Tbs Dijon mustard
1 Tbs plus 1 tsp sherry vinegar
1/2 tsp honey
1/2 tsp coarse salt
1/4 cup extra virgin olive oil

1   Preheat the oven to 450° F. Toss broccoli with 3 tablespoons oil, and season with salt and pepper. Spread on a baking sheet and roast until broccoli begins to soften and brown, about 15 minutes.

2   Heat oil in a small saucepan over medium heat. Add shallot, and cook until translucent, 5 minutes. Stir in chickpeas, and season with salt. Cook for 1 minute. Add vinegar and cook until liquid has evaporated, about 1 minute.

3   In a dry sauté pan over medium heat, toast the walnuts, stirring constantly, about 3 minutes or until fragrant and slightly golden (add a touch of honey if you wish to sweeten them up).

4 In a small bowl, whisk together mustard, vinegar, honey, and salt. Pour in oil in a slow, steady stream, whisking constantly until emulsified.

5 Arrange components on a platter and drizzle lightly with vinaigrette. Serve with remaining vinaigrette on the side.

Servings: 6

Nutrition (per serving): 371 calories, 27.3g total fat, 28.1g carbohydrates, 5.4g fiber, 2.2g sugar, 8.7g protein, 7390IU vitamin a, 48.6mg vit. c, 103.9mg calcium, 3.3mg iron, <1mg vit. b6, 223.3mcg folate, 397.9mg sodium, 699.7mg potassium.

Versatile Salad

I call this salad "versatile" because it can be made with any number of different vegetables. The dressing can be made up to 2 weeks in advance and stored in the fridge.

1/2 pound whole wheat rotini
3 cups green leaf lettuce, chopped
3 cups red leaf lettuce, chopped
1/3 cup corn, canned or frozen and thawed
1 large carrot, peeled and shredded (1/2 cup)
2 stalks celery, diced
2 scallions, chopped
1/4 cup sliced almonds
1/2 cup extra virgin olive oil
2 tsp Dijon mustard
2 1/2 Tbs red wine vinegar
salt and freshly ground black pepper, to taste

1 Cook rotini in a large pot of boiling salted water until al dente. Drain and let cool.

2 In a large salad bowl, toss the lettuces, corn, carrots, celery, scallions and almonds.

3 In a separate small bowl, whisk the extra virgin olive oil, red wine vinegar, mustard, and salt and pepper. Whisk until well combined.

4 Add pasta to large salad bowl and toss with desired amount of Dijon vinaigrette.

Servings: 6

Nutrition (per serving): 354 calories, 22g total fat, 35.7g carbohydrates, 2.7g fiber, 1.5g sugar, 8.2g protein, 2634.9IU vitamin a, 13mg vitamin c, 84.7mg calcium, 2.8mg iron, <1mg vit. b6, 67mcg folate, 70.2mg sodium, 390.6mg potassium.

Grilled Vegetable Antipasto Platter, p. 61

Sandwiches and Burgers

Bagel with Hummus and Veggies

1 whole grain bagel, toasted
1/4 cup hummus
4 slices cucumber
3 slices red bell pepper, optional
2 slices pickles, optional
3 rings jarred sweet banana pepper
1/4 cup alfalfa sprouts or baby spinach leaves
salt and freshly ground black pepper, to taste

1 This sandwich tastes good with a number of toppings. Use what you have on hand. Smear toasted bagel with hummus and top with remaining ingredients.

Servings: 1

Nutrition (per serving): 262 calories, 6.9g total fat, 41.6g carbohydrates, 6.8g fiber, 1.9g sugar, 12.2g protein, 2879.9IU vitamin a, 9.7mg vitamin c, 65.5mg calcium, 4.2mg iron, <1mg vit. b6, 170mcg folate, 729.6mg sodium, 429.8mg potassium.

Hummus and Grilled Vegetable Wrap

2 zucchini, cut lengthwise into 1/4-inch thick slices
2 tsp extra virgin olive oil
1/8 tsp salt
pinch freshly ground black pepper
1 cup store-bought hummus
4 pieces whole wheat wrap bread (9 inches in diameter)
1/4 cup pine nuts
2 jarred roasted red peppers, drained, rinsed, and quartered
2 oz baby spinach leaves (2 cups lightly packed)
1/2 cup red onion, thinly sliced into half moons

1   Preheat the grill or grill pan over medium heat. Brush both sides of the zucchini slices with the oil and sprinkle with the salt and pepper. Grill until tender and slightly browned, about 4 minutes per side.

2   Spread 1/4 cup of the hummus over each piece of bread. Sprinkle 1 tablespoon of pine nuts on top. Top with 3 slices of zucchini, 2 pieces of red pepper, 1/2 cup of the spinach, and a few sliced onions. Roll each of them up and cut in half on a diagonal.

Servings: 4

Nutrition (per serving): 277 calories, 15.5g total fat, 28.8g carbohydrates, 7.9g fiber, 7.6g sugar, 10.7g protein, 1904.1IU vit. a, 32.6mg vit. c, 79.1mg calcium, 3.8mg iron, <1mg vit. b6, 126.1mcg folate, 479.1mg sodium, 612.9mg potassium.

Toasted Guacamole Sandwich

1 small whole wheat hogi roll
1/3 cup guacamole
1 button mushroom, sliced
1–2 slices tomato
1/4 cup sliced black olives
1/2 tsp oregano, dried
1 1/2 tsp Italian dressing
1/4 cup mixed baby greens, washed and drained

1   Preheat the oven to 400° F. Slice roll horizontally and lay flat on a baking sheet. On one side place a layer of sliced mushrooms and top with layer of sliced tomato and then the sliced olives. Drizzle over the Italian dressing and then sprinkle on the oregano.

2   On the other side of the bread, spread a thick layer of guacamole.

3   Bake in oven for about 5 minutes or until slightly toasted. Put greens on top and close sandwich. Serve immediately.

Servings: 1

Nutrition (per serving): 382 calories, 23.5g total fat, 39.7g carbohydrates, 10.5g fiber, 3.2g sugar, 8g protein, 700.9IU vit. a, 31.7mg vit. c, 161.6mg calcium, 4.3mg iron, <1mg vit. b6, 129.5mcg folate, 1003.3mg sodium, 701.1mg potassium.

Veggie Burgers

1/2 cup bulgur
1/2 cup boiling water
2 Tbs extra virgin olive oil, divided
3 cloves garlic, minced
1/2 cup red onion, minced
1 1/2 tsp ground cumin
1 tsp dried oregano
2 Tbs chopped walnuts
1/2 cup fresh spinach leaves, chopped
1 can (15 oz) black beans, rinsed and drained
2 Tbs white wine vinegar

1   Place the bulgur in a small bowl. Add the boiling water and let stand 20–25 minutes. Heat 2 tsp oil in a nonstick skillet over medium heat. Add the garlic and sauté for 1 minute. Stir in the red onion and sauté for 5 minutes until the onion begins to soften. Stir in the cumin, oregano, and walnuts; cook 45 seconds. Add the spinach and cook 30 seconds or until the spinach is wilted.

2   Combine the beans and vinegar in a medium bowl. Mash well with a fork. Stir in the bulgur and onion-spinach mixture and mix well. Taste the mixture for seasoning and add salt and pepper if desired. Cover and place in the fridge for at least 1 hour.

3   Heat the remaining 4 tsp of oil in a large skillet. Remove the bean mixture from fridge and quickly shape into 6 equal patties. Cook patties in the skillet for 3 minutes on each side. Enjoy on a bun with your favorite toppings.

Servings: 4

Nutrition (per serving): 175 calories, 6.5g total fat, 23.5g carbohydrates, 7.6g fiber, <1g sugar, 7.6g protein, 392.6IU vitamin a, 2.1mg vit. c, 49.1mg calcium, 2.6mg iron, <1mg vit. b6, 112.3mcg folate, 198.9mg sodium, 318.8mg potassium.

Exotic Spinach Salad, p. 135

Sauces and Dressings

Dijon Vinaigrette

This is a great staple to have in the fridge. It is so simple, but it is especially delicious tossed with mixed baby greens.

> 1/2 cup extra virgin olive oil
> 2 tsp Dijon mustard
> 2 1/2 Tbs red wine vinegar
> salt and freshly ground black pepper, to taste

1 Whisk together vinegar, salt and pepper, and Dijon. While whisking, stream in olive oil.

Nutrition (per serving): 121 calories, 13.6g total fat, <1g carbohydrates, <1g fiber, 0g sugar, <1g protein, 0IU vitamin a, 0mg vitamin c, 1.5mg calcium, <1mg iron, 0mg vitamin b6, <1mcg folate, 16.1mg sodium, 6.5mg potassium.

Indonesian Peanut Sauce

This sauce is great over Asian-style noodles or served as a dip for grilled tofu or vegetables.

> 2 tsp peanut oil
> 1 large shallot, minced
> 1 clove garlic, minced
> 1/2 tsp red pepper flakes, or to taste
> 1/2 cup creamy peanut butter
> 1/2 cup light coconut milk
> 1 Tbs low sodium soy sauce
> 1 tsp honey
> 2 tsp fresh lime juice

1 Heat oil in saucepan over medium-low heat. Sauté shallot in oil 2 minutes, or until beginning to soften. Add garlic and red pepper flakes, and sauté 1 minute more, or until just fragrant.

2 Whisk in peanut butter, coconut milk, soy sauce, honey, and 1/2 cup water until smooth, and bring to a boil. Reduce heat to medium-low and simmer for 5 minutes. Stir in lime juice. Serve hot or at room temperature. The sauce will keep up to a week in the fridge.

Servings: 10

Nutrition (per serving): 139 calories, 9.9g total fat, 10.5g carbohydrates, <1g fiber, 1.8g sugar, 4.6g protein, 509.2IU vitamin a, 3.8mg vitamin c, 23.4mg calcium, 1.1mg iron, <1mg vit. b6, 25.1mcg folate, 125.6mg sodium, 248.7mg potassium.

Roasted Tomato Dressing

This dressing is delicious over mixed greens, pasta, or as a dipping sauce for bread.

1 pint cherry tomatoes
1 clove garlic, smashed
1 Tbs extra virgin olive oil plus 1/8 cup
salt and freshly ground black pepper
1 Tbs red wine vinegar
1 tsp agave nectar

1   Preheat oven to 350° F. Lay tomatoes and smashed garlic clove in a single layer on a baking sheet. Drizzle with 1 tablespoon olive oil and sprinkle with salt and pepper. Roast in oven for 18–23 minutes or until tomatoes have burst and juices are slightly caramelized.

2   In a blender, add the tomatoes, garlic, and pan juices. Also, add the red wine vinegar and agave nectar and blend. Stream in remaining olive oil (you may need to use slightly more or less depending on desired consistency). Blend until well-combined. Taste for seasoning. May be stored in the refrigerator for 1 week.

Servings: 8

Nutrition (per serving): 41 calories, 3.5g total fat, 2.7g carbohydrates, <1g fiber, <1g sugar, <1g protein, 242IU vitamin a, 7.5mg vitamin c, 2.8mg calcium, <1mg iron, <1mg vitamin b6, 5.9mcg folate, 3.7mg sodium, 90.1mg potassium.

Sweet Dijon Viniagrette

This is my mom's favorite dressing.

> 1/2 cup extra virgin olive oil
> 2 1/2 Tbs red wine vinegar
> 1 Tbs honey
> 2 tsp Dijon mustard
> salt and freshly ground black pepper

1 Whisk together vinegar, salt, pepper, honey, and Dijon. While whisking, stream in olive oil.

Servings: 8

Nutrition (per serving): 129 calories, 13.6g total fat, 2.5g carbohydrates, <1g fiber, 2.2g sugar, <1g protein, 0IU vitamin a, <1mg vitamin c, 1.6mg calcium, <1mg iron, 0mg vitamin b6, <1mcg folate, 16.2mg sodium, 7.8mg potassium.

Vanilla Spice Oatmeal, p. 95

Sides

Corn Salad

1 can (11 oz) corn, drained
2 radishes, chopped
1/2 orange bell pepper, chopped
1 stalk celery, chopped
1 large carrot, peeled and chopped
2 green onions, chopped
1/4 cup Italian dressing

1   Mix all ingredients in a large bowl and chill for at least 20
minutes before serving. Serve cold or at room temperature.

Servings: 4

Nutrition (per serving): 93 calories, 4.7g total fat, 13g carbohydrates, 2.1g fiber,
4.7g sugar, 1.7g protein, 2901.3IU vitamin a, 41.5mg vitamin c, 21.5mg calcium,
<1mg iron, <1mg vit. b6, 37mcg folate, 355.5mg sodium, 244.2mg potassium.

Farro with Pesto

Farro is a delicious Italian whole grain. It is a lot like barley. Look for it at health stores or specialty stores.

>8 cups vegetable broth
>1 pound farro
>2 cups fresh parsley
>1/4 cup fresh basil leaves
>2 Tbs fresh thyme
>2 cloves garlic
>1/3 cup extra virgin olive oil
>1 Tbs red wine vinegar
>3/4 tsp salt
>1/2 tsp freshly ground black pepper

1 Bring the vegetable broth to a boil in a large saucepan over high heat. Add the farro and stir to combine. Reduce the heat to low and simmer the farro, covered, until tender, about 25 minutes. Drain farro and set aside in a large bowl.

2 Meanwhile, in a food processor combine the parsley, basil, thyme, and garlic. Pulse until the herbs are roughly chopped. Add the olive oil, vinegar, salt, and pepper. Pulse again until the herbs make a coarse mixture.

3 Toss the warm farro with the coarse pesto. Transfer to a serving bowl and serve.

Servings: 10

Nutrition (per serving): 342 calories, 11.3g total fat, 51.7g carbohydrates, 10g fiber, <1g sugar, 10.2g protein, 4458.1IU vitamin a, 20.9mg vitamin c, 62.7mg calcium, 4mg iron, <1mg vit. b6, 43.5mcg folate, 1487.2mg sodium, 569.4mg potassium.

Grilled Artichokes

3 artichokes
3 tsp extra virgin olive oil
3 tsp salt
1 1/2 tsp freshly ground black pepper

1   Bring a large pot of salted water to a boil, add the artichokes and simmer for 45 minutes to 1 hour, or until tender.

2   Remove and chill in the fridge for 2 hours or up to a day ahead.

3   Cut artichokes into four, cutting vertically down through the heart.

4   Drizzle the cut sides of each artichoke with oil, salt and pepper.

5   Heat a grill or grill pan to medium-high heat and place artichokes cut side down on grill. Grill for 3–4 minutes or until golden brown. Turn artichoke to the other cut side and grill another 3–4 minutes. Serve hot.

Servings: 6

Nutrition (per serving): 51 calories, 2.4g total fat, 7.1g carbohydrates, 3.4g fiber, <1g sugar, 2.2g protein, 107.8IU vitamin a, 6.1mg vitamin c, 30mg calcium, <1mg iron, <1mg vitamin b6, 30.7mcg folate, 1361.6mg sodium, 219.3mg potassium.

Pineapple and Watermelon

1 pineapple, cut into bite-sized pieces
1/3 cup fresh basil, thinly sliced
1 lime, juiced
1/2 watermelon, cut into bite-sized pieces

1 Mix pineapple pieces with basil and lime juice. Place watermelon pieces in serving dish and pour pineapple over top. Do not stir together.

2 Garnish with fresh basil and lime.

Servings: 8

Nutrition (per serving): 115 calories, <1g total fat, 29.3g carbohydrates, 2g fiber, 23.1g sugar, 2.1g protein, 1735.2IU vitamin a, 46mg vitamin c, 30.8mg calcium, <1mg iron, <1mg vit. b6, 18.9mcg folate, 3.6mg sodium, 397.8mg potassium.

Sesame Brown Rice

1 cup medium-grain brown rice
kosher salt
2 tsp sesame seeds
1 tsp Asian sesame oil
1 Tbs thinly sliced green onion tops

1 In a saucepan over high heat, bring 2 3/4 cups water to a boil. Add the rice and 1/2 tsp salt. Stir once, then reduce heat to low. Cover and cook, without stirring, until the water has been absorbed and the rice is tender, 35–45 minutes.

2 Meanwhile, in a small, dry frying pan over medium heat, toast the sesame seeds until they are fragrant and have taken on color, about 2 minutes. Pour the seeds onto a plate and set aside.

3 Carefully lift the cover of the saucepan so that no condensation drips into the rice. Drizzle the sesame oil evenly over the top and sprinkle on half of the sesame seeds. Gently fluff the rice with a chopstick or the handle of a wooden spoon.

4 Spoon the rice onto the serving dish and sprinkle the remaining sesame seeds and green onion on top. Serve at once.

Servings: 4

Nutrition (per serving): 191 calories, 3.2g total fat, 36.6g carbohydrates, 1.8g fiber, <1g sugar, 3.9g protein, 15.1IU vitamin a, <1mg vitamin c, 31.4mg calcium, 1.1mg iron, <1mg vitamin b6, 11.9mcg folate, 72.8mg sodium, 138.5mg potassium.

Snacks

Dried Fruit and Nut Health Bars

1 cup pitted dates (9 oz)
1 1/2 cups old-fashioned oats
1 cup pecans
1/2 cup macadamia nuts, peeled
1 cup assorted dried fruit (papaya, mango,
   apricot, cherry, blueberry)
2 Tbs oat bran
3 Tbs flaxseed meal (finely ground flaxseed)
2 Tbs wheat germ
1/2 tsp salt
1/2 tsp cinnamon
4 tsp honey

1 Preheat the oven to 350° F. Place dates in a small saucepan, cover with cold water, and bring to a simmer. Drain. Set aside.

2 In a food processor, pulse oats until ground into a coarse meal. Pour oats into a large mixing bowl.

3 Put pecans and macadamia nuts in the food processor and pulse until they are coarsely chopped. Add nuts to ground oats.

4 Put dried fruit into food processor and pulse until fruit is in pea-sized pieces. Add to mixing bowl.

5 Add remaining ingredients, except dates and honey, to the mixing bowl and mix.

6   Purée dates in food processor until smooth. Add date purée and honey to the mixing bowl and mix together until well combined.

7   Grease an 8-inch square baking dish and press mixture into the pan. Bake until center is firm and edges are golden, about 25 mintues. Let cool completely before cutting into bars. Makes 8 bars. Store bars individually wrapped in clear plastic food wrap at room temperature.

Servings: 8

Nutrition (per serving): 391 calories, 19.1g total fat, 55.5g carbohydrates, 9.5g fiber, 14.7g sugar, 7.2g protein, 904.1IU vitamin a, 1.8mg vitamin c, 57.4mg calcium, 3mg iron, <1mg vit. b6, 31.7mcg folate, 155.3mg sodium, 596.7mg potassium.

Fruit and Spicy Nut Trail Mix

1/2 cup raw cashews
1/2 cup raw whole almonds with skin
2 tsp extra virgin olive oil
1 tsp chili powder
1/2 tsp coarse salt
1/2 tsp dried oregano
1/2 tsp paprika
1/4 tsp onion powder
1/4 tsp freshly ground black pepper
1 cup salted roasted soy nuts
1/4 cup salted roasted sunflower seeds
1 cup unsweetened dried apricot pieces
1 cup unsweetened dried apple slices, chopped
1/2 cup dried corn (such as Just Corn)

1 Preheat the oven to 375° F. Combine the first 9 ingredients (through black pepper) in a bowl and toss until blended. Place the coated nuts on a small, nonstick baking sheet and bake for 7–10 minutes or until roasted, turning the nuts once about halfway through.

2 Combine the spicy nuts and remaining ingredients in a medium bowl and stir to combine. Store at room temperature in an airtight container.

Servings: 18

Nutrition (per serving): 107 calories, 6g total fat, 12.1g carbohydrates, 1.5g fiber, 5.5g sugar, 2.8g protein, 256.4IU vitamin a, <1mg vitamin c, 18.2mg calcium, <1mg iron, <1mg vit. b6, 11.6mcg folate, 78.1mg sodium, 181.1mg potassium.

Soup

Taco Soup, p. 180

African Peanut Stew

1 Tbs extra virgin olive oil
1 medium yellow onion, chopped
1 medium green bell pepper, seeded and chopped
1 large clove garlic, minced
1 Tbs honey
1 Tbs peeled and grated fresh ginger
1/2 tsp ground cumin
1 1/2 pounds butternut or other winter squash, peeled, seeded, and cut into 1-inch chunks (about 4 cups)
1 1/4 cups hot water
1/4 tsp black pepper
1 tsp salt
1 can (19 oz) chickpeas, rinsed and drained
1/4 cup smooth natural peanut butter
1/2 cup chopped roasted peanuts
1/4 cup chopped fresh parsley or cilantro

1 Heat the olive oil in a large saucepan over medium heat. Add the onion, cover, and cook until softened, about 5 minutes.

2 Add the bell pepper and garlic, cover, and cook until softened, about 5 minutes. Stir in the honey, ginger, and cumin and cook, stirring for 30 seconds. Add the squash and stir to coat. Add 1 cup hot water, the salt and pepper. Bring to a boil.

3 Meanwhile, mix the remaining 1/2 cup hot water with the peanut butter, then add to the squash mixture in the pot. Cover and reduce the heat to low and simmer until the vegetables are nearly tender, about 15 to 20 minutes.

4   Add chickpeas and roasted peanuts and continue cooking for another 10 minutes. Stir in parsley or cilantro just before removing from heat. Serve immediately.

Servings: 6

Nutrition (per serving): 306 calories, 14.6g total fat, 39.1g carbohydrates, 5g fiber, 8.4g sugar, 10.3g protein, 15453.3IU vit. a, 41.1mg vitamin c, 98.7mg calcium, 2.4mg iron, <1mg vit. b6, 99.2mcg folate, 626.5mg sodium, 727.3mg potassium.

Black Bean and Butternut Squash Soup

1 cup dried black beans
1 large onion, chopped
2 cloves garlic, minced
1 small butternut squash, about 1 pound
1 green bell pepper, seeded and diced
1 tsp dried oregano
1/4 tsp caraway seeds
1/2 cup lager beer (can be replaced with
    apple cider or orange juice)
kosher salt and freshly ground black pepper

1 Soak the beans in water 4 hours or overnight. Place the drained beans in a large saucepan and add 4 cups water. Bring to a boil over high heat, reduce the heat to low, cover, and simmer gently until almost tender but still quite firm, about 1 hour.

2 Add the onion and garlic to the beans, re-cover and continue to cook over low heat until the beans are tender, about 30 minutes longer.

3 Cut the squash in half, remove and discard the seeds, then peel the flesh. Cut the flesh into 1-inch cubes. Add the squash, bell pepper, oregano, caraway seeds and beer to the pan, raise the heat to medium, and cook, uncovered, until the squash and beans are soft but still hold their shape, about 30 minutes. Stir in 1/2 tsp salt and season with pepper.

4 Ladle the stew into warmed bowls and serve at once.

Servings: 4

Nutrition (per serving): 255 calories, <1g total fat, 50.6g carbohydrates, 11g fiber, 6.1g sugar, 12.5g protein, 12120.1IU vit. a, 55.9mg vit. c, 136.3mg calcium, 3.6mg iron, <1mg vit. b6, 257.9mcg folate, 80.9mg sodium, 1256.6mg potassium.

Creamy Vegetable Soup

Try this with cauliflower, broccoli, asparagus, carrot, or any other favorite vegetable.

1 medium onion, chopped
1 stalk celery, chopped
1 clove garlic, thinly sliced
1 Tbs extra virgin olive oil
4 cups rougly chopped vegetable of choice
5 cups water
2 Tbs light miso (or 2 vegetable bouillon cubes)
1 1/2 Tbs tahini
salt and freshly ground black pepper, to taste

1   In a large pot, saute onion, celery, and garlic in olive oil over medium heat for about 2 minutes. Add vegetable of choice and cook 1 minute. Add water and miso. Bring to a boil. Purée soup with a hand blender or in a stand blender. Return to pot and stir in tahini. Season with salt and pepper, to taste. Do not let the soup boil after being puréed. Serve warm or cold.

Servings: 4

Nutrition (per serving): 120 calories, 6.7g total fat, 12.7g carbohydrates, 4.1g fiber, 4.5g sugar, 4.4g protein, 75.4IU vitamin a, 48.9mg vitamin c, 69.1mg calcium, <1mg iron, <1mg vit. b6, 74mcg folate, 370.5mg sodium, 420.6mg potassium.

Curried Yellow Split Pea Soup

1 Tbs canola oil
1 medium onion, chopped
2 tsp garlic, minced
2 medium carrots, chopped
2 stalks celery, chopped
1 medium zucchini, cut into 1/2-inch dice
2 tsp medium curry powder or garam masala
1/2 tsp ground cumin
1/2 tsp ground coriander
2 1/2 cups yellow split peas
2 quarts water
1 tsp sea salt
1/4 tsp white pepper
1 tsp extra virgin olive oil
1 large red bell pepper, cut into 1/2-inch dice
2 medium apples, chopped
cilantro, optional

1   Heat canola oil in a large pot. Sauté onion, garlic, carrots, celery, zucchini, curry powder, cumin, and coriander until vegetables are soft and spices give off fragrance. Add water, peas, salt and pepper and bring to a boil.

2   Separately, in a small sauté pan, sauté the red bell pepper in the olive oil until tender, then add the apples to the pepper.

3   Add sautéed peppers and apples to the soup. Garnish with cilantro.

Servings: 8

Nutrition (per serving): 276 calories, 3.4g total fat, 48.1g carbohydrates, 18.3g fiber, 11.4g sugar, 16.2g protein, 2784.4IU vit. a, 48.4mg vit. c, 64.8mg calcium, 3.3mg iron, <1mg vit. b6, 191.3mcg folate, 273.3mg sodium, 865.1mg potassium.

Green Pea Soup with Cashew Cream

1 cup diced celery
1 1/2 cups chopped white onion
1 Tbs extra virgin olive oil
4 cups shredded romaine lettuce
1 Tbs honey
6 cups water
1/2 tsp dried thyme
1/2 teaspoon dried basil
1 Tbs light miso or 1 vegetable bouillon cube
4 cups frozen petite peas
2 Tbs raw cashews
salt and freshly ground black pepper, to taste

1 In a large soup pot, sauté celery and onions in olive oil over medium heat for 3 minutes. Add lettuce and braise for 2 minutes, until limp. Add honey, water, thyme, basil, and bouillon.

2 Bring soup to a boil, then stir in peas. Return to a boil, cover, and simmer until peas are tender, about 10 minutes.

3 Blend soup with cashews until desired consistency is reached. Season with salt and pepper. Do not let boil. Serve warm or chilled.

Servings: 6

Nutrition (per serving): 164 calories, 5.2g total fat, 24.1g carbohydrates, 6.1g fiber, 11g sugar, 7.2g protein, 4283.1IU vit. a, 29.7mg vitamin c, 63.4mg calcium, 2.6mg iron, <1mg vit. b6, 119.6mcg folate, 240.1mg sodium, 390.2mg potassium.

Hearty Peasant Soup

2 Tbs extra virgin olive oil
1 medium onion, finely chopped
4 cloves garlic, minced
coarse salt
ground pepper
2 Tbs tomato paste
2 Tbs balsamic vinegar
2 cans (15 oz) diced tomatoes in juice
2 cans (15 oz) cannellini beans, rinsed and drained
1 bunch (1 pound) broccoli rabe, cut into 1 inch pieces
4 thick slices rustic whole wheat bread, toasted

1   Heat oil in a large saucepan over medium heat and add onion and garlic. Season with salt and pepper; cook, stirring frequently, until onion is softened, 4 to 5 minutes.

2   Add tomato paste and vinegar; cook, stirring frequently, until slightly darkened, 2 to 3 minutes.

3   Add tomatoes (with juice), beans, broccoli rabe, and 4 cups of water. Bring to a boil, reduce heat to medium, and simmer, stirring occasionally, until broccoli rabe is tender, 8 to 10 minutes. Season with balsamic vinegar, salt, and pepper to taste.

4   To serve, place a slice of toasted bread in the bottom of each serving bowl; ladle soup over toast.

Servings: 6

Nutrition (per serving): 426 calories, 7.4g total fat, 73.4g carbohydrates, 17g fiber, 9.4g sugar, 22.4g protein, 2127.2IU vit. a, 42.4mg vit. c, 300mg calcium, 10.5mg iron, <1mg vit. b6, 96.1mcg folate, 587.2mg sodium, 1972.6mg potassium.

Lentil and Spinach Soup

1 Tbs canola oil
2 medium onions, chopped
1 tsp garlic, minced
4 stalks celery, chopped
2 medium carrots, chopped
1 medium zucchini, cut into 1/2-inch dice
1 1/2 tsp dried basil
1/2 tsp dried thyme
1 bay leaf
2 cups brown lentils, washed
2 quarts water
1 tsp salt
1/2 tsp black pepper
4 cups spinach or kale

1 Sauté first 9 ingredients until soft. Add lentils and water and bring to a boil. Simmer until lentils are done, about 45 minutes.

2 Add salt and pepper and spinach. Remove bay leaf and serve.

Servings: 8

Nutrition (per serving): 209 calories, 2.4g total fat, 34.5g carbohydrates, 16.7g fiber, 5.5g sugar, 14.9g protein, 3531IU vitamin a, 15.3mg vitamin c, 77.5mg calcium, 5.2mg iron, <1mg vit. b6, 262mcg folate, 344.7mg sodium, 748.9mg potassium.

Minestrone

6 cups vegetable broth
3 cups water
1 cup dry red wine
1 can (28 oz) plum tomatoes, chopped, juices included
2 medium carrots, thinly sliced
1 medium onion, chopped
1 medium zucchini, chopped
2 stalks celery, chopped
1 tsp dried basil
1 tsp dried oregano
1 tsp dried thyme leaves
salt and freshly ground black pepper, to taste
1 can (15 oz) kidney beans, rinsed and drained
2 cups shredded cabbage or spinach
1/2 cup whole wheat small pasta shells

1 In a large pot, combine all the ingredients except beans, cabbage (or spinach) and pasta. Bring to a boil over high heat then reduce to low and simmer, partially covered for 1 hour, stirring occasionally.

2 Add the beans and cabbage and cook, covered, for 10 minutes. Add the pasta and cook uncovered until the pasta is al dente, about 8 minutes more.

3 Serve with a drizzle of extra virgin olive oil and crusty whole wheat bread, if desired.

Servings: 6

Nutrition (per serving): 165 calories, <1g total fat, 29.6g carbohydrates, 7.2g fiber, 8.6g sugar, 6.4g protein, 3020.9IU vitamin a, 38.2mg vitamin c, 103.7mg calcium, 2.8mg iron, <1mg vit. b6, 74.8mcg folate, 395.4mg sodium, 806.6mg potassium.

Southern Soup

2 Tbs extra virgin olive oil
1 large leek, white and light green parts, chopped
2 cloves garlic, minced
1 Tbs poultry seasoning
8 oz kale, tough stems removed,
   leaves cut into 2-inch pieces
1 can (15 oz) diced tomatoes, with juice
1 can (15 oz) diced tomatoes, with chilies
3/4 cup dried black-eyed peas
7 cups water
1 quart low sodium vegetable broth or water
3/4 cup whole wheat farfalle (bowtie pasta)

1   Heat oil in a large pot over medium heat. Add leek and sauté 6 minutes, or until soft. Add garlic and poultry seasoning, and sauté 1 minute more. Stir in kale and cook 5 minutes, until leaves are wilted.

2   Add tomatoes, black-eyed peas, vegetable broth and water, then season with salt and pepper. Cover, reduce heat to medium low and simmer 40–45 minutes. Stir in pasta and cook another 7 minutes or until al dente and black-eyed peas are tender.

Servings: 8

Nutrition (per serving): 151 calories, 4.1g total fat, 24.7g carbohydrates, 4.6g fiber, 2.9g sugar, 6.6g protein, 5438.3IU vitamin a, 53.3mg vitamin c, 111.2mg calcium, 2.4mg iron, <1mg vit. b6, 107mcg folate, 327.8mg sodium, 653.9mg potassium.

Spiced Coconut and Red Lentil Soup

A handheld immersion blender makes quick work of puréeing this yellow-hued soup in the pot.

2 tsp extra virgin olive oil
2 cups chopped onion
1 Tbs minced peeled fresh gingerroot
1 tsp ground cumin
1/2 tsp ground coriander
1/8 tsp ground cinnamon
5 cloves garlic, minced
3 cups low sodium vegetable broth
1 cup dried small red lentils
1/2 cup water
1 cup light coconut milk
3 Tbs chopped fresh basil
2 Tbs fresh lime juice
1/4 tsp salt

1   Heat oil in a large saucepan over medium heat. Add onion; cook 12 minutes or until golden. Stir in ginger and next 4 ingredients (through garlic); cook 1 minute, stirring constantly. Add broth, lentils, and 1/2 cup water; bring to a boil. Cover, reduce heat, and simmer 25 mintues or until lentils are tender. Purée soup, either with immersion blender or in batches in a regular blender. If using a regular blender, return puréed mixture to pan. Stir in coconut milk and remaining ingredients. Cook over medium heat for 2 minutes. Serve.

Servings: 4

Nutrition (per serving): 291 calories, 9.8g total fat, 39.3g carbohydrates, 16.2g fiber, 6.2g sugar, 15.5g protein, 135.9IU vit. a, 12.5mg vit. c, 68.9mg calcium, 6.4mg iron, <1mg vit. b6, 231.4mcg folate, 160.7mg sodium, 694.9mg potassium.

Spicy Vegetarian Chili

2 Tbs canola oil
1 1/2 cups chopped yellow onions
1 cup chopped red pepper
2 Tbs minced garlic
1 serrano pepper, seeded and minced
1 medium zucchini, chopped
2 cups fresh corn kernels (about 3 ears) or frozen corn
1 pound white button mushrooms, chopped
2 Tbs chili powder
1 Tbs ground cumin
1 1/4 tsp salt
1 tsp cayenne pepper
1 can (15 oz) diced tomatoes, drained
1 can (15 oz) black beans, rinsed and drained
1 can (15 oz) tomato sauce
1 cup vegetable stock, or water
1/4 cup chopped fresh cilantro

1   In a large heavy pot, heat the oil over medium-high heat. Add the onions, garlic, and peppers. Cook until soft, about 3 minutes. Add zucchini, corn, and mushrooms. Cook another 6 minutes. Add the seasonings and stir until fragrant, about 30 seconds. Add tomatoes and stir well. Add the beans, tomato sauce, and vegetable stock or water. Bring to a boil. Reduce heat and simmer for 20 minutes, stirring occasionally.

2   Remove from heat and stir in cilantro. Adjust the seasoning, to taste. Serve with brown rice, avocado and green onion.

Servings: 10

Nutrition (per serving): 174 calories, 6.3g total fat, 29.1g carbohydrates, 9.2g fiber, 6.7g sugar, 7.8g protein, 6627.6IU vitamin a, 25.9mg vitamin c, 62.5mg calcium, 3.3mg iron, <1mg vit. b6, 86.6mcg folate, 603mg sodium, 885.9mg potassium.

Split Pea and Tomato Soup with Spinach

2 Tbs extra virgin olive oil
2 medium onions, chopped
3 cloves garlic, minced
2 carrots, chopped
2 stalks celery, chopped
1 can (28 oz) diced tomatoes, with juice
3 cups vegetable broth
1 cup dried split peas
2 Tbs fresh parsley, chopped
1 tsp fresh thyme
1 bay leaf
1/8 tsp cayenne pepper
salt and freshly ground black pepper, to taste
2 cups fresh spinach leaves, chopped
1/4 cup chia seeds

1   In a large pot over medium heat, sauté the onions, garlic, carrots, and celery in olive oil, about 7 minutes.

2   Add tomatoes, vegetable broth (and more water if soup is too thick), split peas, fresh parsley, thyme, bay leaf, cayenne, salt, and pepper. Cook until peas are tender (1 1/2 to 2 hours).

3   Add spinach and chia seeds and cook another 10–20 minutes.

Servings: 6

Nutrition (per serving): 273 calories, 7g total fat, 43.8g carbohydrates, 13.8g fiber, 10.8g sugar, 12.1g protein, 5699.8IU vitamin a, 31mg vitamin c, 114.5mg calcium, 3.2mg iron, <1mg vit. b6, 148mcg folate, 735.9mg sodium, 1004.5mg potassium.

Taco Soup

2 Tbs extra virgin olive oil
1 jalapeno chile, stemmed and minced
1 onion, diced
2 cloves garlic, minced
3/4 cup brown rice, uncooked
1 1/2 tsp ground cumin
1 tsp dried oregano
1 tsp dried thyme
1/2 tsp garlic powder
1/4 tsp cayenne pepper
1 can (15 oz) diced tomatoes in juice
1/2 cup prepared salsa
1 quart vegetable broth
1 can (15 oz) black beans, rinsed and drained
1 can (15 oz) white or red kidney beans, rinsed and
   drained
1 can (11 oz) corn, drained
salt and pepper
avocados
green onion, sliced
cilantro, chopped

1   Sauté jalapeno, onion, and garlic in a large pot over medium
    heat. Cook until soft, about 5 minutes. Add seasoning and
    rice. Stir together. Add canned ingredients, broth and salsa.
    Bring to a boil and simmer, covered, for 45–60 minutes.
    Serve with avocado, green onion, and cilantro.

Servings: 8

Nutrition (per serving): 270 calories, 4.7g total fat, 47.8g carbohydrates, 9.3g fiber,
4.4g sugar, 11.8g protein, 238.2IU vitamin a, 14mg vitamin c, 112.6mg calcium,
4.8mg iron, <1mg vit. b6, 73.7mcg folate, 365.3mg sodium, 910.8mg potassium.

Tomato Soup

1 medium onion, chopped
1 medium carrot, peeled and chopped
1 stalk celery, chopped
2 Tbs extra virgin olive oil
2 cloves garlic, minced
1/2 tsp sweet paprika
1 tsp Italian seasoning
1 can (28 oz) fire-roasted tomatoes (I prefer Muir Glen)
1 can (28 oz) whole tomatoes, with juices
1 bay leaf
1 tsp agave nectar or honey
1 tsp sherry vinegar
1 cup water
1/4 cup fresh parsley, chopped
basil, chopped

Homemade croutons
4 slices whole wheat bread
1/4 cup extra virgin olive oil
salt and freshly ground black pepper

1   In a dutch oven or heavy pot, heat the olive oil and sauté onion, celery, carrot, and garlic over medium heat for about 5 minutes. Add Italian seasoning, paprika, canned tomatoes, bay leaf, agave nectar, sherry vinegar, and water. Bring to a boil then reduce to a simmer. Simmer for about 15 minutes.

2   Discard bay leaf. Add parsley and season with salt and pepper. Run soup through a food mill or blend with a hand

blender or food processor. Serve with fresh basil and a handful of homemade croutons.

3 To make the croutons, preheat oven to 400° F. Cube the bread into 1-inch cubes and toss with olive oil. Season liberally with salt and pepper. Spread in a single layer on a baking sheet and bake for 7–10 minutes or until golden and toasted.

Servings: 6

Nutrition (per serving): 215 calories, 13g total fat, 24g carbohydrates, 4.6g fiber, 13g sugar, 4.5g protein, 1932.2IU vitamin a, 29.8mg vitamin c, 113.2mg calcium, 3.6mg iron, <1mg vit. b6, 43.2mcg folate, 453.9mg sodium, 651.1mg potassium.

Tuscan Bean Soup

1 cup dried borlotti or cranberry beans,
   soaked and drained
1/2 head savoy cabbage, about 1 pound
2 Tbs extra virgin olive oil
1 large yellow onion, chopped
2 cloves garlic, minced
1 large carrot, peeled and chopped
1 stalk celery, thinly sliced
1 can (28 oz) chopped or diced tomatoes
1 bay leaf
pinch red pepper flakes, optional
kosher salt and freshly ground black pepper
8 slices day-old coarse country bread

1   Place the soaked, drained beans in a saucepan, and add water to cover generously. Bring to a boil over high heat, reduce the heat to low, cover partially, and simmer gently until tender, 1–1 1/2 hours. Remove from the heat and drain, reserving the beans and liquid separately.

2   Cut the half head of cabbage in half again to form 2 wedges, then cut the wedges crosswise into strips 1/2-inch wide.

3   In a large Dutch oven over medium-high heat, warm the olive oil. Add the onion, garlic, and celery and sauté until the onion and celery are translucent, about 6 minutes. Add the cabbage strips and stir until they wilt, about 5 minutes. Add the tomatoes and their liquid and stir to combine.

4   Measure the bean cooking liquid and add water as needed to total 4 cups. Add the beans and liquid to the pan along with the bay leaf and red pepper flakes, if using. Bring to a boil over medium-high heat, reduce the heat to medium-low and

simmer until the beans are heated through, about 10 minutes. Stir in 1/4 tsp salt and season with black pepper.

5 Remove the bay leaf from the soup and discard. Ladle the soup into the bowls and serve with a slice of bread.

Servings: 8

Nutrition (per serving): 234 calories, 5.2g total fat, 39.9g carbohydrates, 11.4g fiber, 7.6g sugar, 10.9g protein, 2123.1IU vit. a, 21mg vit. c, 106.7mg calcium, 3.7mg iron, <1mg vit. b6, 206.5mcg folate, 335.5mg sodium, 831.7mg potassium.

Vegetable Soup with Beans

1 Tbs extra virgin olive oil
1 onion, chopped
1 carrot, peeled and chopped
1 stalk celery, chopped
4 cups vegetable broth
1 can (15 oz) diced tomatoes, with juice
2 cups shredded cabbage or spinach
1 zucchini, chopped
2 Tbs chia seeds or barley
2 Tbs fresh oregano leaves (or 1 tsp dried)
1 tsp fresh thyme (or 1/2 tsp dried)
1/2 cup adzuki beans, canned
1/2 cup kidney beans, canned
1/2 cup chickpeas, canned

1 Heat olive oil in a large heavy-bottom stock pot and sauté onion, carrot, and celery for 5 minutes. Add remaining ingredients to the pot. Rinse and drain beans before adding them. Simmer together for 30 minutes. Serve.

Servings: 6

Nutrition (per serving): 379 calories, 5.8g total fat, 67g carbohydrates, 15.1g fiber, 6.6g sugar, 18.2g protein, 4775IU vit. a, 35.8mg vit. c, 188.5mg calcium, 7.1mg iron, <1mg vit. b6, 115.7mcg folate, 1457mg sodium, 1601.5mg potassium.

Tomato Soup, p. 181

A-Z Cheat Sheets

The following charts are unique because they show nutrients per 100 calories, not per gram. This shows the nutrient density of foods. Foods with high nutrient density give you the most nutrients for the least amount of calories. These charts show you how to get the most "bang" for your calorie when it comes to Iron (Fe), Calcium (Ca), Vitamin B12, and Protein.

A-Z Cheat Sheet
Nuts

	Gram Weight per 100 cal.	Fe	Ca	B12	Protein
Nuts, almond butter, w/ salt	16	0.6	43	0	2.4
Nuts, almonds, dry roasted, w/ salt	17	0.8	45	0	3.7
Nuts, almonds, oil roasted, w/ salt	16	0.6	48	0	3.5
Nuts, Brazil nuts	15	0.4	24	0	2.2
Nuts, cashew butter, w/ salt	17	0.9	7	0	3
Nuts, cashews, dry roasted w/ salt	17	1	8	0	2.7
Nuts, cashews, raw	18	1.2	7	0	3.3
Nuts, chestnuts, Chinese, raw	45	0.6	8	0	1.9
Nuts, chestnuts, European, roasted	41	0.4	12	0	1.3
Nuts, coconut meat, flakes, sweetened	22	0.3	2	0	0.7
Nuts, coconut meat, raw	28	0.7	4	0	0.9
Nuts, coconut milk, canned	51	1.7	9	0	1
Nuts, coconut water (liquid from coconuts)	526	1.6	126	0	3.7
Nuts, hazelnuts	16	0.7	18	0	2.4
Nuts, macadamia, dry roasted, w/ salt	14	0.4	10	0	1.1
Nuts, macadamia, raw	14	0.5	12	0	1.1
Nuts, pecans	14	0.4	10	0	1.3
Nuts, pecans, dry roasted, w/ salt	14	0.4	10	0	1.3
Nuts, pine nuts	15	0.8	2	0	2
Nuts, pistachio nuts, dry roasted w/ salt	18	0.8	19	0	3.8
Nuts, pistachio nuts, raw	18	0.7	19	0	3.7
Nuts, walnuts, black	16	0.5	10	0	3.9
Nuts, walnuts, English	15	0.4	15	0	2.3
Seeds, chia, dried	20	0	129	0	3.2
Seeds, flaxseed	19	1.1	48	0	3.4
Seeds, pumpkin and squash seed kernels, dried	18	2.8	8	0	4.5
Seeds, sesame butter, tahini	18	0.4	74	0	3.1
Seeds, sesame seed kernels	16	1	10	0	3.2
Seeds, sesame seeds, whole	17	2.5	170	0	3.1
Seeds, sunflower seed kernels	17	0.9	13	0	3.6

A-Z Cheat Sheet
Fruits

	Gram Weight per 100 cal.	Fe	Ca	B12	Protein
Apple juice, unsweetened, w/ ascorbic acid	212	0.9	15	0	0.1
Apples, raw, w/ skin	192	0.2	12	0	0.5
Applesauce, unsweetened w/ ascorbic acid	233	0.3	7	0	0.4
Apricot nectar, w/ ascorbic acid	179	0.7	13	0	0.7
Apricots, raw	208	0.8	27	0	2.9
Avocados, raw, California	60	0.4	8	0	1.2
Avocados, raw, Florida	83	0.1	8	0	1.7
Bananas, raw	112	0.3	6	0	1.2
Blackberries, raw	233	1.4	67	0	3.2
Blueberries, raw	175	0.5	11	0	1.3
Cherries, sweet, raw	159	0.6	21	0	1.7
Clementines, raw	213	0.3	64	0	1.8
Cranberries, dried, sweetened	32	0.2	3	0	0.02
Cranberries, raw	217	0.5	17	0	0.8
Cranberry juice, unsweetened	217	0.5	17	0	0.8
Dates, medjool	36	0.3	23	0	0.6
Fig, raw	135	0.5	47	0	1
Grape juice, unsweetened	164	0.4	15	0	0.9
Grapefruit juice, pink, raw	256	0.5	23	0	1.3
Grapefruit juice, white, canned, unsweetened	263	0.5	18	0	1.4
Grapefruit, pink and red, raw	270	0.2	30	0	1.4
Grapes, red or green, raw	145	0.5	14	0	1
Guava, raw	147	0.4	26	0	3.7
Jujube, dried	35	0.6	28	0	1.3
Kiwi fruit, raw	164	0.5	56	0	1.8
Lemon juice, raw	400	0.1	28	0	15.2
Lemons, raw, w/ peel	500	3.5	305	0	6
Lime juice, raw	400	0.4	56	0	1.6
Limes, raw, w/o peel	333	2	110	0	2.3
Mango nectar, canned	196	0.7	33	0	2.1
Mangos, raw	154	0.2	15	0	0.8
Melon, cantaloupe, raw	294	0.6	26	0	2.5
Melon, honeydew, raw	278	0.5	17	0	1.5
Nectarines, raw	227	0.6	14	0	2.4
Olives, pickled, green	69	0.3	36	0	0.7
Olives, ripe, canned	87	2.9	77	0	0.7
Orange juice, raw	222	0.4	24	0	1.5

	Gram Weight per 100 cal.	Fe	Ca	B12	Protein
Oranges, raw	213	0.2	85	0	2
Papayas, raw	256	0.3	62	0	1.6
Peach nectar, canned, w/ ascorbic acid	185	0.4	9	0	0.5
Peaches, canned w/ light syrup	238	0.7	12	0	1
Peaches, raw	256	0.6	15	0	2.3
Pear nectar, canned w/ ascorbic acid	167	0.4	8	0	1.8
Pear, Asian, raw	238	0	1	0	1.2
Pears, canned, light syrup	213	0.4	15	0	0.6
Pears, raw	172	0.3	16	0	6.5
Pineapple juice, canned, unsweetened	189	0.6	25	0	6.8
Pineappple, canned, light syrup	192	0.8	27	0	6.9
Pineapple, raw	200	0.6	26	0	1
Plums, canned, purple, light syrup	159	1.4	14	0	0.6
Plums, raw	217	0.4	13	0	1.5
Pomegranates, raw	147	0.4	4	0	1.4
Prune puree	39	1.1	12	0	0.8
Raisins, seedless	33	0.6	2	0	1
Raspberries, raw	192	1.3	48	0	2.3
Strawberries, raw	313	1.3	50	0	2.1
Tangerines, mandarin oranges, canned in juice	270	0.8	30	0	1.7
Tangerines, raw	189	0.3	70	0	1.5
Watermelon, raw	333	0.8	23	0	2

A-Z Cheat Sheet
Vegetables

	Gram Weight per 100 cal.	Fe	Ca	B12	Protein
Alfalfa seeds, sprouted, raw	435	4.3	139	0	17.4
Artichokes, boiled w/ salt	489	1.1	40	0	5.5
Arugula, raw	400	6	640	0	10.4
Asparagus, boiled	455	4.1	105	0	10.9
Beans, Fava, in pod, raw	114	1.7	42	0	9
Beans, Kidney, cooked w/ salt	303	2.7	58	0	14.5
Beans, Lima, canned	141	2.2	39	0	5.6
Beans, Navy, cooked w/ salt	128	2.6	21	0	9
Beans, Pinto cooked w/ salt	500	3	75	0	9
Beans, snap green, canned, drained no added salt	500	4.5	130	0	5.5
Beans, snap green, raw	323	3.2	119	0	5.8
Beets, boiled	227	1.8	36	0	3.9
Broccoli, boiled w/o salt	286	1.7	114	0	6.8
Broccoli, florets, raw	357	3.1	171	0	10.4
Brussels sprouts, boiled, w/ salt	278	3.3	100	0	7
Cabbage, Chinese, raw	769	6.2	808	0	11.5
Cabbage, common, raw	417	2.5	196	0	5
Carrot, baby, raw	286	2.6	91	0	1.7
Carrots, raw	244	0.7	80	0	2.2
Carrot, boiled w/o salt	286	0.9	86	0	2
Cauliflower, raw	400	1.6	88	0	7.6
Celery, raw	625	1.2	250	0	4.4
Chard, Swiss, boiled w/o salt	500	11.5	290	0	9.5
Chives, raw	333	5.3	307	0	11
Cilantro, raw	435	7.4	291	0	9.1
Corn, sweet, white, canned, drained	123	1	6	0	3.2
Corn, on cob, boiled w/ salt	125	4.4	5	0	3.4
Cucumber, raw	667	2	107	0	4
Edamame, frozen, prepared	82	1.9	52	0	9
Eggplant, boiled w/o salt	286	0.7	17	0	2.3
Endive, raw	588	4.7	306	0	7
Fennel bulb, raw	322	2.3	158	0	3.9
Garlic, raw	67	1.1	121	0	4.3
Ginger root, raw	125	0.8	20	0	2.3
Kale, boiled w/ salt	357	3.2	257	0	6.8
Leeks, boiled w/ salt	322	3.5	97	0	2.6
Lentils, cooked w/o salt	99	3.1	14	0	8.7

	Gram Weight per 100 cal.	Fe	Ca	B12	Protein
Lettuce, butterhead, boston, bibb, raw	769	10	269	0	10
Lettuce, romaine, raw	588	5.9	194	0	7
Lettuce, iceberg, raw	714	2.9	129	0	6.4
Lettuce, red leaf, raw	625	7.5	206	0	8
Lima Beans	141	2.3	39	0	5.8
Mushroom, oyster, raw	233	3	7	0	7.7
Mushrooms, crimini, raw	370	1.5	67	0.4	9.3
Mushrooms, portabella, raw	384	2.3	31	0.2	9.6
Mushrooms, shiitake, cooked w/o salt	178	0.8	5	0	2.8
Mushrooms, white, raw	455	2.3	14	0.2	14
Mustard greens, boiled, w/o salt	667	4.6	493	0	15.3
Okra, boiled, w/o salt	455	1.4	350	0	8.6
Onions, raw	250	0.5	58	0	2.7
Onions, scallions, raw	313	4.7	225	0	5.6
Parsley, raw	278	17.2	383	0	8.3
Parsnips, boiled, w/o salt	141	0.8	52	0	1.8
Peas, snow, sugar snap, raw	238	5	102	0	6.6
Peas, green, raw	123	1.8	31	0	6.6
Peas, sprouted, raw	78	1.8	28	6.3	6.9
Pepper, serrano, raw	313	2.5	34	0	5.3
Peppers, hot chili, green, raw	250	3	45	0	5
Peppers, hot chili, red, raw	250	2.5	35	0	4.7
Peppers, jalapeno, raw	333	2.3	33	0	4.3
Peppers, sweet, green, raw	500	1.7	50	0	4
Peppers, sweet, red, raw	323	1.4	23	0	3.2
Peppers, sweet, yellow, raw	370	1.7	41	0	3.7
Potatoes, russet, flesh and skin, baked	103	1	19	0	2.7
Potatoes, red, flesh and skin, baked	112	0.8	10	0	2.6
Pumpkin, canned, w/o salt	294	4.1	76	0	3.2
Radicchio, raw	435	2.6	83	0	6.1
Radishes, raw	625	2.1	156	0	4.4
Shallots, raw	139	1.7	51	0	3.5
Soybeans, green, cooked w/salt	71	1.8	103	0	8.8
Spinach, boiled w/o salt	435	15.6	591	0	13
Spinach, raw	435	11.7	430	0	12.6
Squash, summer, boiled w/o salt	500	2	135	0	4.5
Squash, zucchini, boiled, w/skin, w/o salt	625	2.2	81	0	3.7
Squash, winter, acorn, baked w/o salt	179	1.6	79	0	2
Squash, winter, butternut, baked w/o salt	250	1.5	103	0	2.3
Squash, winter, spaghetti, baked, w/o salt	370	1.1	78	0	2.4
Sweet potato, baked in skin, w/o salt	111	0.8	42	0	2.2
Tomatillos, raw	313	1.9	22	0	2.8
Tomato sauce, canned	417	4.2	54	0	5.4
Tomatoes, crushed, canned	313	4.1	106	0	5
Tomatoes, red, raw	555	1.7	55	0	5

	Gram Weight per 100 cal.	Fe	Ca	B12	Protein
Turnip greens and turnips, boiled w/o salt	286	5	366	0	8.6
Waterchestnuts, Chinese, raw	103	0.1	11	0	1.4
Watercress, raw	909	1.8	1091	0	21
Yam, baked, w/o salt	86	0.4	12	0	1.3
Yeast extract spread	63	2.3	54	0.3	17.6

A-Z Cheat Sheet
Grains

	Gram Weight per 100 cal.	Fe	Ca	B12	Protein
Amaranth	27	2	41	0	3.9
Arrowroot flour	28	0.1	11	0	0.1
Barley flour or meal	29	0.1	9	0	3
Barley, hulled	28	1	9	0	3.5
Barley, pearled, cooked	81	0.8	9	0	1.9
Buckwheat	29	0.6	5	0	3.8
Buckwheat flour, whole-groat	30	1.2	12	0	3.7
Bulgur, cooked	120	1.1	12	0	3.7
Corn flour, degermed, unenriched, yellow	27	0.2	1	0	1.5
Corn flour, masa, enriched, yellow	27	2	0.4	0	2.6
Corn flour, whole-grain, white	28	0.7	2	0	1.9
Corn, white	27	0.7	2	0	2.6
Corn, yellow	27	0.7	2	0	2.6
Cornmeal, degermed, enriched, yellow	27	1.1	1	0	2
Cornmeal, whole-grain, yellow	28	1	2	0	2.2
Cornstarch	26	0.1	1	0	0.1
Couscous, cooked	89	0.4	7	0	3.4
Macaroni, cooked, enriched	63	0.8	4	0	3.7
Macaroni, whole-wheat, cooked	80	0.9	12	0	4.3
Millet, cooked	84	0.5	3	0	2.9
Noodles, egg, cooked, enriched	72	1.1	9	0	3.3
Noodles, egg, spinach, cooked, enriched	76	0.8	14	0.11	3.8
Noodles, Japanese, soba, cooked	101	0.5	4	0	5.1
Oat bran, cooked	250	2.3	25	0	8
Oats	26	1.2	0.1	0	4.3
Pasta, fresh-refrigerated	35	1.1	5	0.11	3.9
Pasta, fresh-refrigerated, cooked	76	0.8	5	0.11	131
Pasta, fresh-refrigerated, spinach, cooked	78	0.8	14	0.11	3.9
Quinoa, cooked	83	1.3	14	0	3.7
Rice noodles, cooked	92	0.1	4	0	0.8
Rice, brown, long-grain, cooked	90	0.4	9	0	2.3
Rice, brown, medium-grain, cooked	89	0.5	9	0	2
Rice, white, long-grain, enriched, cooked	81	1.5	15	0	2.4
Rice, white, long-grain, regular, cooked	77	0.9	8	0	2.1
Rice, white, short-grain, cooked	77	1.2	1	0	1.8
Rye flour, dark	31	2	17	0	4.3
Rye flour, light	27	0.5	6	0	2.3

	Gram Weight per 100 cal.	Fe	Ca	B12	Protein
Semolina, enriched	28	1.2	5	0	3.5
Spelt, cooked	79	1.3	8	0	4.3
Wheat bran, crude	46	4.9	34	0	7.2
Wheat flour, white, all-purpose, enriched, bleached	27	1.3	4	0	2.8
Wheat flour, whole-grain	29	1.1	10	0	4
Wheat germ, crude	28	1.7	11	0	6.4
Wheat, durum	29	1	10	0	4
Wheat, hard red spring	30	1.1	8	0	4.7
Wheat, hard red winter	31	1	9	0	3.9
Wheat, hard white	29	1.3	9	0	3.3
Wheat, soft red winter	30	1	8	0	3.1
Wheat, soft white	29	1.6	10	0	3.1
Wheat, sprouted	51	1.1	14	0	3.8
Wild rice, cooked	99	0.6	3	0	4

A-Z Cheat Sheet
Legumes

	Gram Weight per 100 cal.	Fe	Ca	B12	Protein
Baked Beans, canned w/o salt	95	0.3	48	0	4.6
Baked Beans, canned w/ pork	94	1.6	50	0	4.9
Beans, black, boiled w/o salt	76	1.6	20	0	6.7
Beans, cranberry, canned	120	1.9	41	0	6.6
Beans, French, boiled w/o salt	78	0.8	49	0	5.5
Beans, great northern, canned	88	1.4	46	0	6.5
Beans, kidney, canned	119	1.4	40	0	6.2
Beans, kidney, boiled, w/o salt	79	1.7	28	0	6.8
Beans, navy, canned	88	1.6	42	0	6.6
Beans, pink, boiled, w/o salt	67	1.5	35	0	6.1
Beans, pinto, canned	116	1.7	50	0	5.6
Beans, pinto, boiled w/o salt	70	1.5	32	0	6.3
Beans, small white, boiled w/o salt	70	2	51	0	6.3
Beans, white, canned	88	2.6	64	0	6.4
Beans, yellow, boiled, w/o salt	69	1.7	43	0	6.4
Broadbeans (fava beans), canned	141	1.4	37	0	7.7
Chickpeas (garbanzo beans), canned	84	1.1	27	0	4.1
Chickpeas (garbanzo beans) boiled w/o salt	61	1.8	30	0	5.4
Cowpeas (blackeyes, southern), canned	130	1.3	26	0	6.1
Fatafel, home-prepared	30	1	16	0	4
Hummus, commercial	60	1.4	23	0	4.8
Lentils, boiled, w/o salt	86	2.9	16	0	7.8
Lima beans, large, canned	127	2.3	27	0	6.2
Miso	50	1.3	29	0.04	5.9
Mung beans, boiled, w/o salt	95	1.3	26	0	6.7
Peanut butter, smooth, reduced fat	20	0.4	673	0	5
Peanuts, all types, boiled, w/ salt	31	0.3	17	0	4.3
Peanuts, all types, dry-roasted, w/ salt	17	0.4	9	0	4.1
Peanuts, all-types, oil-roasted, w/ salt	17	0.3	10	0	4.7
Peanuts, all-types, raw	18	0.8	16	0	4.5
Peas, split, boiled, w/o salt	84	1.1	12	0	7.1
Refried beans, canned	106	1.7	37	0	5.9
Soybean, curd cheese	66	3.7	125	0	8.3
Soybean, mature seeds, dry roasted	22	0.9	31	0	8.7
Soymilk, lowfat, w/ calcium, vit A & D	244	1.1	200	0	3.9
Tofu, extra firm, prepared w/ nigari	110	2	192	0	10.9
Veggie burgers, or soyburgers	56	1.4	77	1.1	8.9

Endnotes

1. American Heart Association (2006). Diet and Lifestyle Recommendations Revision. Retrieved August 3, 2009 from the World Wide Web: http://circ.ahajournals.org/cgi/reprint/CIRCULATIONAHA.106.176158

2. The normal medical treatment for high cholesterol is to prescribe a drug in the statin class.

3. The Vegan Wolf (2009). Retrieved July 15, 2009 from the World Wide Web: http://www.veganwolf.com/index.html

4. Vegan Society (2009). Vegan Society History. Retrieved July 20, 2009 from the World Wide Web: http://www.vegansociety.com/html/about_us/history/

5. Albert Einstein. In Defense of Animals. Retrieved July 15, 2009 from the World Wide Web: http://www.idausa.org/

6. Physicians Committee for Responsible Medicine and Vegetarian Times (2007). Vegetarian Starter Kit. Retrieved May 11, 2009, from the World Wide Web: http://www.vegetariantimes.com

7. Dwyer, J T. (1988) Health aspects of vegetarian diets. *American Journal of Clinical Nutrition, 48*: pp.712–738.

8. Vegetarian Times (2007). Why Go Veg? Retrieved May 11, 2009 from the World Wide Web: http://www.vegetariantimes.com/resources/why_go_veg/

9. Taber, L. A., & R. A. Cook (1980). Dietary and anthropometric assessment of adult omnivores, fish-eaters and lacto-ovo-vegetarians. *Journal of the American Dietetic Association, 76:* pp. 21–29.

10. Havala, S., & J. T. Dwyer (2009). Position of the American Dietetic Association: Vegetarian Diets. *Journal of the American Dietetic Association, 109* (7): pp. 1266–1282.

11. Dwyer, J. T. (1988). Health aspects of vegetarian diets. *American Journal of Clinical Nutrition, 48:* pp. 712–38.

12. Physicians Committee for Responsible Medicine and Vegetarian Times (2007). Vegetarian Starter Kit. Retrieved May 11, 2009, from the World Wide Web: http://www.vegetariantimes.com

13. Varshney, V. P., M. Bedi, & B. Bhandari (2005). Effect of non-vegetarian diet on cardiovascular reactivity to mental stress in young adults.

Vascular Disease Prevention, 2 (4): pp. 293–298

14. Sacks, F. M., et al. (1974). Blood pressure in vegetarians. *American Journal of Epidemiology, 100*: pp.390–398.

15. Vegetarian Times, September 2009, p. 18.

16. Campbell, C., & T. Campbell (2005). *The China Study.* Dallas: BenBella Books, p. 23.

17. Campbell, C., & T. Campbell (2005). *The China Study.* Dallas: BenBella Books, p. 21.

18. Vegetarian Times (2007). Why Go Veg? Retrieved May 11, 2009 from the World Wide Web: http://www.vegetariantimes.com/resources/why_go_veg/

19. McCredie, S. (2009). Go Vegetarian to Save Money. *MSN money.* Retrieved October 20, 2009 from the World Wide Web: http://articles.moneycentral.msn.com/SavingandDebt/SaveMoney/GoVegetarianToSaveMoney.aspx

20. I realize that occasionally fruits and vegetables are unclean as well, and I advocate thoroughly washing your groceries to minimize this risk. Vegetarian Times (2007). Why Go Veg? Retrieved May 11, 2009 from the World Wide Web: http://www.vegetariantimes.com/resources/why_go_veg/

21. CDC (2009). Morbidity and mortality weekly report. *CDC* 58 (22): pp. 609-15.

22. Physicians Committee for Responsible Medicine and Vegetarian Times (2007). Vegetarian Starter Kit. Retrieved May 11, 2009, from the World Wide Web: http://www.vegetariantimes.com

23. PETA (2009). Vegetarian Starter Kit. Retrieved July 31, 2009 from the World Wide Web: http://www.goveg.com/order.asp

24. U.S. EPA. (2004). Pesticides: The EPA and Food Security. EPA. Retrieved July 12, 2009 from the World Wide Web: http://www.factory-farm.org/human-health-impact/

25. PETA (2009). Vegetarian Starter Kit. Retrieved July 31, 2009 from the World Wide Web: http://www.goveg.com/order.asp

26. PETA (2009). Vegetarian Starter Kit. Retrieved July 31, 2009 from the World Wide Web: http://www.goveg.com/order.asp

27. Campbell, C., & T. Campbell (2005). *The China Study.* Dallas: BenBella Books, p. 58.

28. Campbell, C., & T. Campbell (2005). *The China Study.* Dallas: BenBella Books, p. 58.

29. Campbell, C., & T. Campbell (2005). *The China Study.* Dallas: BenBella Books, p. 58.

30. Campbell, C., & T. Campbell (2005). *The China Study.* Dallas: BenBella Books, p. 58.

31. Physicians Committee for Responsible Medicine and Vegetarian Times (2007). Vegetarian Starter Kit. Retrieved May 11, 2009, from the World Wide Web: http://www.vegetariantimes.com

32. Campbell, C., & T. Campbell (2005). *The China Study*. Dallas: BenBella Books, p. 31.

33. Campbell, C., & T. Campbell (2005). *The China Study*. Dallas: BenBella Books, p. 31.

34. Campbell, C., & T. Campbell (2005). *The China Study*. Dallas: BenBella Books, p. 58.

35. Campbell, C., & T. Campbell (2005). *The China Study*. Dallas: BenBella Books, p. 58.

36. Physicians Committee for Responsible Medicine and Vegetarian Times (2007). Vegetarian Starter Kit. Retrieved May 11, 2009, from the World Wide Web: http://www.vegetariantimes.com

37. Physicians Committee for Responsible Medicine and Vegetarian Times (2007). Vegetarian Starter Kit. Retrieved May 11, 2009, from the World Wide Web: http://www.vegetariantimes.com

38. Willett, W., P. Skerrett, & Harvard School of Public Health (2005). *Eat, Drink, and Be Healthy*. NY: Free Press, p.131.

39. Vegetarian Times (2007). Why Go Veg? Retrieved May 11, 2009 from the World Wide Web: http://www.vegetariantimes.com/resources/why_go_veg/

40. PETA (2009). Vegetarian Starter Kit. Retrieved July 31, 2009 from the World Wide Web: http://www.goveg.com/order.asp

41. Alewaeters, K., P. Clarys, M. Hebbelinck, P. Deriemaeker, & J.P. Clarys (2005). Cross-sectional analysis of BMI and some lifestyle variables in Flemish vegetarians compared with non-vegetarians. *Ergonomics, 48* (11): pp. 1433-1444.

42. PETA (2009). Vegetarian Starter Kit. Retrieved July 31, 2009 from the World Wide Web: http://www.goveg.com/order.asp

43. Physicians Committee for Responsible Medicine and Vegetarian Times (2007). Vegetarian Starter Kit. Retrieved May 11, 2009, from the World Wide Web: http://www.vegetariantimes.com

44. PETA (2009). Vegetarian Starter Kit. Retrieved July 31, 2009 from the World Wide Web: http://www.goveg.com/order.asp

45. Vegetarian Times (2007). Why go Veg? Retrieved May 11, 2009 from the World Wide Web: http://www.vegetariantimes.com/resources/why_go_veg/

46. Kolata, G. (2009). Ideas & trends; History of food fervor; Vegetarians vs. Atkins: Diet Wars are almost Religious. *The New York Times*. Retrieved Sept 19, 2009 from the World Wide Web: http://www.nytimes.com/2004/02/22/weekinreview/ideas-trends-history-food-fervor-vegetar-

ians-vs-atkins-diet-wars-are-almost.html

47. Suzuki. M. et al. (2009). Okinawa Centenarian Study. Retrieved July 12, 2009 from the World Wide Web: http://www.okicent.org/index.html

48. Willett, W., P. Skerrett, & Harvard School of Public Health (2005). *Eat, Drink, and Be Healthy.* NY: Free Press, p.137.

49. Gear, J. S. et al. (1979) Symptomless diverticular disease and intake of dietary fibre. *The Lancet, 1*: pp. 511–514.

50. Vegetarian Times (2007). Why Go Veg? Retrieved May 11, 2009 from the World Wide Web: http://www.vegetariantimes.com/resources/why_go_veg/

51. Willett, W., P. Skerrett, & Harvard School of Public Health (2005). *Eat, Drink, and Be Healthy.* NY: Free Press, pp. 143–145.

52. Fairfield, K. M., & R. Fletcher (2002). Vitamins for chronic disease prevention in adults: Scientific review. *JAMA: Journal of the American Medical Association, 287* (23): pp. 3116-3127.

53. Willett, W., P. Skerrett, & Harvard School of Public Health (2005). *Eat, Drink, and Be Healthy.* NY: Free Press, p. 143.

54. Adams, T., A. Fisher, S. Hansen, & S. Hansen (2007). *Maintaining the miracle: an owner's manual for the human body, 4th ed.* Salt Lake City: CAPP Publishing.

55. Medletter Associates. (2005). Vitamins: Sources, actions, and benefits. *Nutrition & Weight Control for Longevity,* January: pp. 20–21.

56. Medletter Associates. (2005). Vitamins: Sources, actions, and benefits. *Nutrition & Weight Control for Longevity,* January: pp. 20–21.

57. Willett, W. et al. (2001). What vitamins should I be taking, Doctor? *New England Journal of Medicine, 345*: pp. 1819–1824.

58. Holick, M. (2007). Vitmain D deficiency. *New England Journal of Medicine, 357*: pp. 226–281.

59. Holick, M. (2007). Vitmain D deficiency. *New England Journal of Medicine, 357*: pp. 226–281.

60. Ingraham B.A., B. Bragdon, & A. Nohe (2007). Molecular basis of the potential of vitamin D to prevent cancer. *Curr Med Res Opin, 24*: 139.

61. Nowson, C. A. (2005). The significance of Vitamin D to health in Australia. *Asia Pacific Journal of Clinical Nutrition, 14*: p. 17.

62. BBC News (2005). Vitamin D "aids lung cancer ops." *BBC News.* 22 April 2005. Retrieved March 2006 from the World Wide Web: http://news.bbc.co.uk/2/hi/health/4458085.stm.

63. Willett, W. et al. (2001). What vitamins should I be taking, Doctor? *New England Journal of Medicine, 345*: pp. 1819–1824.

64. Nowson, C. A. (2005). The significance of Vitamin D to health

in Australia. *Asia Pacific Journal of Clinical Nutrition, 14:* p. 17.

65. Kushi L. H., A. R. Folsom, R. J. Prineas, P. J. Mink, Y. Wu, & R. M. Bostick (1996). Dietary antioxidant vitamins and death from coronary heart disease in postmenopausal women. *New England Journal of Medicine, 334:* pp. 1156-1162.

66. Packer L., S. U. Weber, & G. Rimbach (2001). Molecular aspects of alpha-tocotrienol antioxidant action and cell signalling. *Journal of Nutrition 131* (2): 369–373.

67. Medletter Associates. (2005). Vitamins: Sources, actions, and benefits. *Nutrition & Weight Control for Longevity,* January, pp. 20–21.

68. Adams, T., A. Fisher, S. Hansen, & S. Hansen (2007). *Maintaining the miracle: an owner's manual for the human body, 4th ed.* Salt Lake City: CAPP Publishing.

69. Medletter Associates. (2005). Vitamins: Sources, actions, and benefits. *Nutrition & Weight Control for Longevity,* January: pp. 20–21.

70. Medletter Associates. (2005). Vitamins: Sources, actions, and benefits. *Nutrition & Weight Control for Longevity,* January: pp. 20–21.

71. Medletter Associates. (2005). Vitamins: Sources, actions, and benefits. *Nutrition & Weight Control for Longevity,* January: pp. 20–21.

72. Willett, W. et al. (2001). What vitamins should I be taking, Doctor? *New England Journal of Medicine, 345:* pp. 1819–1824.

73. Medletter Associates. (2005). Vitamins: Sources, actions, and benefits. *Nutrition & Weight Control for Longevity,* January: pp. 20–21.

74. Medletter Associates. (2005). Vitamins: Sources, actions, and benefits. *Nutrition & Weight Control for Longevity,* January: pp. 20–21.

75. Medletter Associates. (2005). Vitamins: Sources, actions, and benefits. *Nutrition & Weight Control for Longevity,* January: pp. 20–21.

76. Fairfield, K. M., & R. Fletcher (2002). Vitamins for chronic disease prevention in adults: Scientific review. *JAMA: Journal of the American Medical Association, 287* (23): pp. 3116–3127.

77. MRC Vitamin Study Research Group (1991). Prevention of neural tube defects: Results of the Medical Research Council Vitamin Study. *Lancet, 338:* pp. 131–137.

78. Willett, W. et al. (2001). What vitamins should I be taking, Doctor? *New England Journal of Medicine 345:* pp. 1819–1824.

79. Welch G.N., & J. Loscalzo (1998). Homocysteine and atherothrombosis. *New England Journal of Medicine 338:* pp. 1042-1050.

80. Willett, W. et al. (2001). What vitamins should I be taking, Doctor? *New England Journal of Medicine 345:* pp. 1819–1824.

81. Fairfield, K. M., & R. Fletcher (2002). Vitamins for chronic disease prevention in adults: Scientific review. *JAMA: Journal of the American Medical Association, 287* (23): pp. 3116–3127.

82. Willett, W. et al. (2001). What vitamins should I be taking, Doctor? *New England Journal of Medicine, 345*: pp. 1819–1824.

83. (2005). Vitamins: Sources, actions, and benefits. *Nutrition & Weight Control for Longevity,* January: pp. 20–21.

84. Vaskonen, T. (2003). Dietary minerals and modification of cardiovascular risk factors. *Journal of Nutritional Biochemistry, 14* (9): pp. 492–507.

85. Adams, T., A. Fisher, S. Hansen, & S. Hansen (2007). *Maintaining the miracle: an owner's manual for the human body, 4th ed.* Salt Lake City: CAPP Publishing.

86. Vaskonen, T. (2003). Dietary minerals and modification of cardiovascular risk factors. *Journal of Nutritional Biochemistry, 14* (9): pp. 492–507.

87. He, F. J., & G. A. MacGregor (2001). Beneficial effects of potassium. *British Medical Journal, 323*: pp. 497–501.

88. Williams G.H., & N. K. Hollenberg (1991). Non-modulating hypertension: A subset of sodium-sensitive hypertension. *Hypertension, 17* (Suppl 1): pp. I81–I85.

89. (2007). Sodium, potassium, and your health. *Nutrition & Weight Control for Longevity,* January: pp. 25–32.

90. Agren, M. S. (1990). Studies on zinc in wound healing. *Acta Dermato-Venereologica Supplementum 154:* pp. 1–36.

91. Turner, Natasha. (2009). The Perils of Sugar. Retrieved on October 19, 2009 from the World Wide Web: http://www.truestarhealth.com/members/archives.asp?content=14ml3p1a95

92. Willett, W., P. Skerrett, & Harvard School of Public Health (2005). *Eat, Drink, and Be Healthy.* NY: Free Press, p. 111.

93. Willett, W., P. Skerrett, & Harvard School of Public Health (2005). *Eat, Drink, and Be Healthy.* NY: Free Press, pp. 110–111.

94. Slavin, J. L. (2000). Whole grains, refined grains and fortified grains: What's the difference? *Asia Pacific Journal of Clinical Nutrition, 9* (supplement), pp. 23–27.

95. Rose, N., K. Hosig, B. Davy, E. Serrano, & L. Davis. (2007). Whole-grain intake is associated with body mass index in college students. *Journal of Nutrition Education & Behavior, 39* (2): pp. 90–94.

96. Vartan, S. (2003). How sweet it isn't. *E: The environmental magazine, 14* (6): pp. 42–43.

97. Mann, Denise. Are Artificial Sweeteners Safe? *WebMD.* Retrieved October 20, 2009 from the World Wide Web: http://www.webmd.com/a-to-z-guides/features/are-artificial-sweeteners-safe

98. Hull, J. S. (2006). Aspartame Symptoms Submitted to the FDA. Retrieved June 12, 2009 from the World Wide Web: http://www.sweetpoi-

son.com/articles/0706/aspartame_symptoms_submit.html

99. Turner, Natasha. (2009). The Perils of Sugar. Retrieved on October 19, 2009 from the World Wide Web: http://www.truestarhealth.com/members/archives.asp?content=14ml3p1a95

100. Martini (2006). Report for Schools, OB-GYN and Pediatricians on Children and Aspartame/MSG, Retrieved on July 12, 2009 from the World Wide Web: http://wnho.net/report_on_aspartame_and_children.htm

101. PETA (2009). Vegetarian Starter Kit. Retrieved July 31, 2009 from the World Wide Web: http://www.goveg.com/order.asp

102. Dowdle, H. (2009). Confessions of a Cheeseaholic. *Vegetarian Times,* September. Retrieved October 2009 from the World Wide Web: http://www.vegetariantimes.com/features/archive_of_editorial/861

103. Dowdle, H. (2009). Confessions of a Cheeseaholic. *Vegetarian Times,* September. Retrieved October 2009 from the World Wide Web: http://www.vegetariantimes.com/features/archive_of_editorial/861

104. Weber, K. (2009). *Food, Inc.* NY: PublicAffairs. 292.

105. AWI (2009). Animals in Agriculture. Animal Welfare Institute. Retrieved October 20, 2009 from the World Wide Web: http://www.awionline.org/ht/d/sp/i/213/pid/213#

106. Mellon M.G., C. Benbrook, & K. L. Benbrook (2001). *Hogging It! Estimates of Antimicrobial Abuse in Livestock.* Cambridge, MA: Union of Concerned Scientists. Retrieved March 12, 2008, from the World Wide Web: http://www.uscus.org/food_and_environment/antibiotics_and_food/hogging-it-estimates-of-antimicrobial-abuse-in-livestock.html.

107. Barnouin, R., & K. Freedman (2008). *Skinny Bitch Bun in the Oven.* Philadelphia, PA: Running Press, p. 95.

108. Barnouin, R., & K. Freedman (2008). *Skinny Bitch Bun in the Oven.* Philadelphia, PA: Running Press, p. 95.

109. U.S. Department of Agriculture. (2007). Dairy 2007. Part 1: reference of diary cattle health and management practices in the United States.Retrieved June 8, 2009 from the World Wide Web: http://www.sphis.usda.gov/vs/ceah/nahms/dairy07/Dairy2007_Part_1.pdf.

110. U.S. Department of Agriculture, Food Safety and Inspection Service (2006). Veal from farm to table. Retrieved May 16, 2008, from the World Wide Web: http://www.fsis.usda.gov/Fact_Sheets/Veal_from_Farm_to_Table/index.asp.

111. Mendl, M. T. (1991). The Effects of alternative forms of intensive pig husbandry on measures of pig welfare. In Bradley, A. & W. L. Sckofield (Eds.), *Proceedings of the First Associatin of Veterinary Students Animal Welfare Symposium* Cambridge, U.K.: Association of Veterinary Students.

112. In Defense of Animals (2009). Factory Farming Facts. Retrieved

July 3, 2009 from the World Wide Web: http://www.idausa.org/facts/factoryfarmfacts.html

113. U.S. Department of Agriculture (2008). Poultry slaughter: 2007 annual summary. National Agricultural Statistics Service. Retrieved September 8, 2008, from the World Wide Web: http://usda.mannlib.cornell.edu/usda/current/PoulSlauSu/PoulSlauSu-02-28-2008.pdf.

114. Dawkins, M.S., & S. Hardie (1989). Space needs of laying hens. *British Poultry Science, 30*: pp. 413–416.

115. www.nal.usda.gov/awic/newsletters/v10n3schw.htm Wedemeyer GA. 1997. Effects of rearing conditions on the health and physiological quality of fish in intensive culture. In Iwama, G.K., A. D. Pickering, J. P. Sumpter, & C. B. Schreck (Eds.), *Fish Stress and Health in Aquaculture, Society for Experimental Biology, Seminar Series 62.* Cambridge, U.K.: Cambridge University Press, pp. 35–71.

116. Maurer A. (2007). Preventing the catfish blues. *Tech Journal South,* March 15. Retrieved February 12, 2008 from the World Wide Web: http://www.Techjournalsouth.com/news/article.html?item_id=2767.

117. PETA (2009). Fish Farms: Underwater Factories. Retrieved Aug 3, 2009 from the World Wide Web: http://fishinghurts.com/fishFarms.asp

118. Willett, W., P. Skerrett, & Harvard School of Public Health (2005). *Eat, Drink, and Be Healthy.* NY: Free Press, p. 50.

119. Willett, W., P. Skerrett, & Harvard School of Public Health (2005). *Eat, Drink, and Be Healthy.* NY: Free Press, p. 50.

120. Willett, W., P. Skerrett, & Harvard School of Public Health (2005). *Eat, Drink, and Be Healthy.* NY: Free Press, p. 52.

121. Beling, S. (1997). *Power Foods.* NY: HarperCollins, p. 188.

122. Willett, W., P. Skerrett, & Harvard School of Public Health (2005). *Eat, Drink, and Be Healthy.* NY: Free Press, p. 170.

123. Willett, W., P. Skerrett, & Harvard School of Public Health (2005). *Eat, Drink, and Be Healthy.* NY: Free Press, p. 170.

124. Barnouin, R., & K. Freedman (2008). *Skinny Bitch Bun in the Oven.* Philadelphia, PA: Running Press, p. 95.

Index